PEARSON   ALWAYS LEARNING

Sandra L. Caron, Ph.D.
The University of Maine

SEX AROUND THE WORLD

Cross-Cultural Perspectives on Human Sexuality

Fifth Edition

Cover Art: Courtesy of Pearson Learning Solutions

Pearson Learning Solutions, 501 Boylston Street, Suite 900, Boston, MA 02116
A Pearson Education Company
www.pearsoned.com

Printed in the United States of America

1 2 3 4 5 6 7 8 9 10 V3NL 17 16 15 14 13

000200010271843553

MC

ISBN 10: 1-269-59084-7
ISBN 13: 978-1-269-59084-6

CONTENTS

PREFACE v

THE COUNTRIES:

AFGHANISTAN 1

AUSTRALIA 4

AUSTRIA 7

BELGIUM 10

BRAZIL 13

BULGARIA 16

CANADA 19

CHILE 22

CHINA 25

COSTA RICA 29

CUBA 32

CZECH REPUBLIC 35

DENMARK 38

EGYPT 41

FINLAND 44

FRANCE 47

GERMANY 50

GREECE 53

HUNGARY 56

INDIA 59

IRAN 63

IRELAND 66

ISRAEL 69

ITALY 72

JAMAICA 75

JAPAN 78

KENYA 81

MEXICO 84

MOROCCO 88

NEPAL 91

NETHERLANDS 94

NEW ZEALAND 97

NORWAY 100

POLAND 103

PORTUGAL 106

ROMANIA 109

RUSSIAN FEDERATION 112

RWANDA 115

SINGAPORE 117

SLOVAKIA 120

SOUTH AFRICA 123

SPAIN 126

SWEDEN 129

SWITZERLAND 132

THAILAND 135

TURKEY 138

UNITED KINGDOM 141

UNITED STATES 145

VIETNAM 150

ZIMBABWE 152

REFERENCES 155

INTERNATIONAL RESOURCES
RELATED TO SEXUALITY 185

PREFACE

Most people could not say that a day goes by in which they do not encounter some aspect of sexuality. We are confronted with issues pertaining to birth control, abortion, AIDS, LGBT rights, and so on in our homes, schools, places of employment and even within our own thoughts. Human sexuality is a widely discussed topic that often becomes the center of conversation in one form or another. Yet, this topic of discussion should not be limited to one's familiar habitat.

Technological advances in communication and the manner in which we access information have linked us to cultures across the world in ways our ancestors never fathomed. The booming popularity of the Internet, for example, allows us the opportunity to connect with people and places of foreign domain via our own personal computers. College students are quite familiar with this convenient method of communicating since most institutions provide access to the Internet through computer clusters often located in campus libraries. These advances have undoubtedly transformed our world into a global village. Therefore, it has become necessary to learn more about other cultures' social, political, economic, and religious values—and yes, sexual attitudes as well.

The purpose of this book is to serve as a quick reference to facts about cross-cultural perspectives in human sexuality. It can also serve as a supplement to courses taught in human sexuality and cross-cultural psychology or development. It is important to educate Americans of the diverse attitudes and behaviors that exist across the world because knowledge about another culture's views assists us in gaining perspective on our own sexuality.

In addition, this book will help to lessen the ethnocentrism used by many Americans when judging other cultures. In other words, it will assist people in understanding that what goes on in America is not the norm and that our own values should not be treated as the standard by which to judge others. It is natural for Americans to think in such a manner since our country is geographically isolated from nearly 200 nations that exist around the world. Yet, we should not forget that we are indeed a Multicultural nation and a melting pot of different beliefs and practices as well as sexual attitudes. For college students, this fact is apparent since 1 out of every 10 students in American colleges comes from other countries. After reading this book, students will learn that sexual behaviors differ among various cultural groups and that there is no set standard for what is considered normal.

This book covers the basic aspects of sexuality for 50 different countries. A brief overview of each country is provided, including information on population, ethnicity, religions, per capita income (this is the GNP divided by the total population, not average income), etc. It is important to have some background knowledge since the environment we live in often plays a major role in shaping our attitudes on sexuality. Pertinent data is then presented on the following issues: sexual activity, contraception, abortion, sexuality education, HIV/AIDS, LGBT issues, prostitution, and pornography. Since each chapter follows the same content outline, the reader can easily draw comparisons between each country.

For instance, among industrialized nations, the United States has one of the leading pregnancy rates for teenagers ages 15–19. For every 1,000 American teenage girls, 68 become pregnant each year. Experts who have become long-time advocates of sex education argue that teaching teenagers about human sexuality could help to diminish the pregnancy rate. However, in America, only 23 states require formal teaching about human sexuality. And in many states, these mandates or polices preclude teaching about such subjects as intercourse, abortion, masturbation, homosexuality, condoms, and safer sex.

In comparison, the Netherlands' teenage pregnancy rate stands at 12 per 1,000 teenagers. Ironically, lessons in human sexuality are available at all levels of school education and offered through youth clubs.

Another striking difference relates to abortions. As American politicians continue the controversial debate on the issue, Russians view abortion as a primary method of birth control. On average, every woman born in the Russian Federation has two or three abortions. It was also the first country in the world to legalize abortion. In Ireland, abortion has only recently become legal in cases where the mother's life is in danger. In February 1992, a 14-year-old rape victim was prevented by the High Court to travel to Britain for an abortion procedure. This eventually led to a Supreme Court ruling that grants women the freedom to travel abroad and obtain abortions. Presently, an estimated 4,000 Irish women journey to Britain for abortions each year.

While detecting the remarkable differences in sexual behaviors among these 50 countries, the reader will also discover some fascinating similarities. For example, most countries have established a minimum age of sexual consent. Adult pornography is regulated by the government and certain laws control access to sexual material. And in all countries, incest is considered a taboo.

Among the following pages, you are presented with an opportunity to explore various perspectives in human sexuality. The facts presented in this book speak for themselves: We live in a world composed of cultural diversity. It is when we perceive the views of others, we also develop a better understanding of the values and behaviors that exist within our own culture and learn to accept our role in the global village.

About the Author

Dr. Sandra L. Caron is Professor of Family Relations/Human Sexuality at the University of Maine. She teaches both undergraduate and graduate courses in family studies and human sexuality. She is also a member of the Women's Studies faculty. For nearly a decade, she taught a summer travel course entitled, Human Sexuality in Europe, which provided students with an international perspective on sexual and reproductive health issues. In this course, U.S. college students traveled to London, Amsterdam and Stockholm to meet with sexuality professionals and see firsthand how other countries deal with teen pregnancy, abortion, birth control, sexuality education, as well as public policy related to HIV/AIDS, LGBT issues and prostitution.

Dr. Caron is the founder and director of three nationally recognized peer education programs: "Athletes for Sexual Responsibility," "The Greek Peer Educator Program," and "Male Athletes Against Violence." She has written a regular column on sexuality for the campus newspaper entitled *Sex Matters,* hosted a radio show by that same name on the campus radio station, and hosts a national website for college students entitled collegesextalk.com (*http://www.collegesextalk.com*).

In 2013, she was the recipient of the Mabel Sine Wadsworth award from the Mabel Wadsworth Women's Health Center in Bangor, Maine for her lifetime contribution to sexual and reproductive health. In 2002, Dr. Caron received the Presidential Public Service Achievement Award for the University of Maine. In 1999 she received the Margaret Vaughn Award from the Family Planning Association of Maine for her outstanding contribution to sexuality education. She is the 1998 recipient of the Presidential Outstanding Teaching Award for the University of Maine. In 1997, she became Maine's first recipient of the Faculty-Student Centered Award. She has been an active member of the American Association of Sex Educators, Counselors, and Therapists, and the Society for the Scientific Study of Sexuality for nearly 30 years.

Her research and publications have focused on the social-sexual development of young people, with an emphasis on sexual decision-making, contraceptive use, safer sex, sexual assault, sexuality education, and cross-cultural perspectives. In addition to her many scholarly publications in research journals, she has authored two books, *Cross-Cultural Perspectives on Human Sexuality* (now in its 5th edition) and *Sex Matters for College Students: FAQs in Human Sexuality, 2nd edition* (published by Prentice Hall). Her newest book released in the Fall of 2013 is, *The Sex Lives of College Students: Two Decades of Attitudes and Behaviors.*

AFGHANISTAN

Major Cities:	Kandahar, Mazar-i-Sharif, Charikar, Herat
Ethnic Groups:	Pashtun 42%, Tajik 27%, Hazara 9%, Uzbek 9%, Aimak 4%, Turkmen 3%, Baloch 2%
Languages:	Afghan Persian or Dari (official) 50%, Pashto (official) 35%, Turkic languages (primarily Uzbek and Turkmen) 11%
Major Religions:	Sunni Muslim 80%, Shia Muslim 19%
GDP per capita (PPP):	$1,100
Urban Population:	24%
Infant Mortality:	119 per 1,000 births
Life Expectancy:	Females: 51 years; Males: 48 years
Adult Literacy:	28%
Health Care System:	1 doctor per 5,000 people. Due to the war, most medical providers left. An estimated one-quarter of the population has no access to health care.

References
❑ *Reference World Atlas* (2013). NY: DK Publishing.
❑ *The World Almanac and Book of Facts 2013* (2012). NY: World Almanac Education Group.
❑ *The World Factbook https://www.cia.gov/library/publications/the-world-factbook/*

Sexual Activity[1]

❖ Age of consent for heterosexual relations is either 18 or when married.
❖ Same-sex relationships are illegal.

Contraception

❖ The Taliban opposes the use of contraceptives, calling them 'illicit and non-Islamic.'[2]
❖ Since the demise of the Taliban in 2002, contraceptive pills and condoms have become increasingly available, especially in the urban areas.[2]
❖ Afghanistan has the highest fertility rate in Asia. The average Afghan woman gives birth to 6–7 children.[3]
❖ Mullahs in Afghanistan are trying new strategies to prevent an ongoing health and economic crisis caused by high fertility and maternal mortality rates: They're passing out birth control pills and distributing condoms.[4]
❖ Health experts say contraception is starting to catch on in the country, which is also facing a maternal death rate that's exceeded only in Sierra Leone.[4]
❖ The stance on contraception in Afghanistan is based on saving lives and reducing economic instability—rather than simply facilitating more sex.[4]

Abortion[5]

❖ Abortion is only legal to save the woman's life.
❖ A person who intentionally causes abortion of a human fetus by beating or any other harmful means shall be sentenced to long imprisonment not exceeding seven years.

Sex Education[6]

❖ Formal sex education is nonexistent. It is a series of warnings; shame and guilt sanctions girls' behavior. An Afghan girl is trained to suppress her own desires.

HIV/AIDS

❖ 1,250 cases of HIV/AIDS inside Afghanistan have been reported to the World Health Organization.[7]
❖ The extrapolated prevalence of STDs in Afghanistan is 6,813,930.[8]

LGBT issues

❖ Same-sex relations are outlawed under Islam and punishable by death as a Hudood crime.[9]
❖ In the past and particularly during the conflict—commanders, tribal leaders and others kept boys for sexual and other purposes. As one study has termed it, "the prevalence of sex between Afghan men is an open secret." The practice of using young boys as objects of pleasure seems to have been more than a rare occurrence. Such relations are often coercive and opportunistic as more influential, older men are taking advantage of the poor economic situation of some families and young males, leaving them with little choice. There are also a few documented cases of abduction of young boys for sexual exploitation by men.[10]

Prostitution

❖ Prostitution is illegal and the punishment for prostitution in Afghanistan is death.[11]
❖ The practice of men dancing at parties is relatively common in Afghanistan, and they are used for sex.[12]

Pornography[13]

❖ Following the fall of the Taliban, access to pornography has flourished. Satellite dishes are springing up on rooftops across the country. Private homes, restaurants and guesthouses are tuning in to 170 channels from all over the world. Four of them show nothing but porn.

Resource

▶ Afghan Family Guidance Association
www.afga.org.af

AUSTRALIA

AUSTRALIA

POPULATION: 22,262,501

CAPITAL: **CANBERRA**

Major Cities:	Sydney, Melbourne, Brisbane, Perth, Adelaide
Ethnic Groups:	Caucasian 92%; Asian 7%; Aboriginal 1%
Languages:	English (official) and aboriginal language
Major Religions:	Protestant 27%, Roman Catholic 26%, other Christian 8%
GDP per capita (PPP):	$43,300
Urban Population:	89%
Infant Mortality:	5 per 1,000 births
Life Expectancy:	Females: 85 years; Males: 80 years
Adult Literacy:	99%
Health Care System:	3 doctors per 1,000 people. Universal health insurance has been available since 1984; private health insurance is also available.

References

❑ *Reference World Atlas* (2013). NY: DK Publishing.
❑ *The World Almanac and Book of Facts 2013* (2012) NY: World Almanac Education Group.
❑ *The World Factbook https://www.cia.gov/library/publications/the-world-factbook/*

Sexual Activity[1]

❖ The age of consent in most states is 16 years old, with one exception: The age of consent for anal sex is 18 in Queensland.

Contraception[2]

❖ The most commonly used methods of contraception are the Pill, IUD, condom, and diaphragm.
❖ Despite nearly 70% of Australian women of reproductive age using a contraceptive method, estimates are that over 50% of Australian women have had an unplanned pregnancy. This rate is similar to that in the United Kingdom (30%) and United States (49%).
❖ Emergency contraception has been available over-the-counter in Australia since 2004 but this has had little effect on the actual use of emergency contraception. Most Australian women remain unaware of the over-the-counter availability of emergency contraception, have misconceptions about it, and want more information from their general practitioners.

Abortion[3]

❖ Only South Australian and Northern Territory laws define lawful abortions. Other states and territories derive laws from judicial interpretation.
❖ All states permit abortions to save the life of the pregnant woman.
❖ All states and territories require that abortions be performed in a hospital and by licensed physicians.
❖ The Australian government health insurance covers abortions.
❖ All states except for Tasmania (Criminal Code Act of 1924) and Western Australia (Criminal Code Act of 1913) permit abortions on mental and physical health grounds.

❖ The maximum prison term for persons performing illegal abortions range from 10–15 years.

Sex Education[4]

❖ In 1992, the Health Minister released a report recommending installing condom vending machines in schools as part of sex education. Many state education officials agreed to read the report and considered integrating condom use and sexuality into their AIDS education material.
❖ At that time, schools run by the Roman Catholic Church agreed to focus on improving AIDS education but not sex education or condom use.

HIV/AIDS

❖ Australia was among the first countries in the world to report AIDS cases.[5]
❖ An estimated 22,000 people were living with HIV/AIDS in Australia in 2011.[5]
❖ Early in the epidemic Australia began offering needle exchange programs to avert HIV transmission through IV drug use.[5]
❖ Males who have sex with men account for more than 80% of new HIV cases.[5]
❖ Australia's epidemic is considerably less severe than those of any other high-income countries.[6]
❖ Overall rates for other STI (Sexually Transmitted Infections) have declined since the mid-1980s. However, rates of STI among indigenous populations continue to be substantially higher (by a factor of 10 to 100 times) than in the non-indigenous population.[5]

LGBT issues

❖ The rights of LGBT individuals have been increasing since the 1970s. In 1970 gays and lesbians established an open organization to demand recognition, equal and just treatment before the law, and an end to discrimination.[7]

❖ In 1972 South Australia became the first state to partially decriminalize homosexual acts.[7]

❖ By 1987 all the states of Australia decriminalized homosexual acts except for Queensland.[7]

❖ In 1992 the Australian cabinet ended its ban on gays in the military.[8]

❖ In March 2002, with the passage of the Acts Amendment (Lesbian and Gay) Law Reform Bill 2001, Western Australia, no longer lagged far behind other Australian states in its recognition of rights on the basis of sexual orientation, but rather set a progressive example. This bill contained measures that equalized the age of consent for all persons at 16 years; repealed the Gross Indecency Law, which targeted male-male sexual activity in public places; included sexual orientation as a protected category in the State's Equal Opportunity Act of 1984; provided access to adoption and in vitro fertilization treatment for same-sex couples; and granted additional rights to same-sex couples.[9]

❖ Since 2009, same-sex individuals and couples receive the same tax and health benefits opposite sex couples.[9]

❖ Starting in 2013, government documents offered transgender individuals a third option for indicating their sex and/or gender beyond "Male" or "Female." They can check off X to indicate "Indeterminant/Intersex/Unspecified." [10]

Prostitution[11]

❖ It is not illegal to sell sex in Australia.

❖ In all jurisdictions, except New South Wales, street prostitution is illegal and workers may be arrested for soliciting or loitering for the purposes of prostitution.

❖ In New South Wales, Australia, any person over the age of 18 may offer to provide sexual services in return for money. In Victoria, Australia, a person who wishes to run a prostitution business must have a license. Prostitutes working for themselves in their own business, as prostitutes in the business, must be registered. Individual sex workers are not required to be registered or licensed.

❖ Except for New South Wales and Victoria, no state penalizes the clients of prostitutes.

Pornography[12]

❖ Child pornography in Australia is a federal offense and is punishable under Australian law.

❖ Australia classifies all films and literature to protect children from pornographic material.

❖ The classifications range from G (general exhibition) to X (explicit sex: restricted to adults 18 and over).

❖ The government cannot impose restrictions on what can be filmed, but can restrict transportation of obscene material.

❖ X-rated videos are not illegal in Australia but to sell them commercially is illegal.

Resource

▶ Sexual Health and Family Planning Australia, *http://www.shfpa.org.au/*

▶ Society for Australian Sexologists, *http://assertnational.org.au/*

AUSTRIA

Major Cities:	Vienna, Graz, Linz, Salzburg, Innsbruck
Ethnic Groups:	Austrians 91%, former Yugoslavs 4% (includes Croatians, Slovenes, Serbs, and Bosniaks)
Languages:	German (official)
Major Religions:	Roman Catholic 74%; Protestant 5%, Islam 4%
GDP per capita (PPP):	$43,100
Urban Population:	68%
Infant Mortality:	4 per 1,000 births
Life Expectancy:	Females: 83 years; Males: 77 years
Adult Literacy:	98%
Health Care System:	National health care system, with nearly universal access. 5 doctors per 1,000 people.

References

❑ *Reference World Atlas* (2013). NY: DK Publishing.
❑ *The World Almanac and Book of Facts 2013* (2012) NY: World Almanac Education Group.
❑ *The World Factbook https://www.cia.gov/library/publications/the-world-factbook/*

Sexual Activity

❖ Age of consent is 14.[1]
❖ One third of the women have had sexual intercourse before the age of 16 years.[2]
❖ Twenty-four percent of 15–44 year olds have had at least one unplanned pregnancy, and 10% have had more than one.[2]

Contraception

❖ Vasectomies as well as vasectomy-reversal procedures are performed less frequently in Austria than in other European countries.[2]
❖ In general the standard of contraception in Austria is rather low; on average only every second Austrian woman uses contraceptives. No data is available on the use of prophylactics by Austrian men.[3]
❖ First Love is an Austrian FPA counseling center dedicated to helping young people. First Love offers free and confidential psychological counseling and gynecological examinations to young women one afternoon per week.[4]
❖ Contraceptives are not supplied free of charge through the State services. Condoms are advertised and available in pharmacies and condom vending machines also exist. There are no practical obstacles to obtaining contraceptives except for adolescents who may not be welcomed by all physicians.[5]
❖ Emergency contraception was introduced in 2010.[6]

Abortion

❖ Since January 1974 abortion on request within the first trimester of pregnancy has been exempt from punishment for the first time in Austrian history.[7]
❖ Although abortion within the first trimester is legal, access to abortion is still not guaranteed throughout Austria. In several parts of the country it is difficult or simply impossible to obtain one because many physicians refuse to perform abortions for moral and/or religious reasons.[7]
❖ All abortions must be performed by a licensed physician. Doctors in private practices perform the majority of abortions.[7]
❖ The health care system pays for abortions performed for medical reasons.[8]
❖ RU-486 (Mifepristone) was approved for marketing in 1999.[9]

Sex Education[10]

❖ Sex education is legally regulated as part of the school curriculum and it is theoretically implemented in elementary, secondary, and higher education levels.
❖ The situation is not reflected in practice, though some sex education is available in some schools according to the willingness of the teaching staff. The mass media regularly features sex education programming.

HIV/AIDS[11]

❖ An estimated 9,000 people are living with HIV/AIDS in Austria. One third of all AIDS cases got infected by injecting drugs, about half are through male-to-male sex.

❖ Austria has one of the highest rates of testing. Testing is mandatory in all blood/plasma organ donors, as well as for prostitutes.

LGBT issues[12]

❖ Austria has a long history of criminalization and oppression of lesbians and gay men. In 1971, Austria was one of the last countries in Europe to repeal the total ban on homosexuality.

❖ Until 1997, gay and lesbian organizations and publications were illegal under Sections 220 and 221 of the Penal Code.

❖ Austria has had a very poor record of anti-discrimination provisions in general and none at all to protect gays and lesbians from sexual-orientation-based discrimination. However, in 2009 they passed a law allowing registered partnerships for same-sex couples.

❖ Austria allows gays to serve in the military.

❖ In 2013, they became the 13th country to allow same-sex second partner adoption.

Prostitution[13]

❖ Prostitution is legal in Austria.

❖ In Vienna, legalized prostitution is tightly controlled by the Board of the Viennese Public Health Service. Registered prostitutes are routinely screened for STIs. Those found to be HIV-positive are prohibited from working.

Pornography[14]

❖ Pornography is regulated through a federal law passed in 1990, "The Federal Act Against Obscene Publications and for the Protection of Youth Morally Endangered." In 1994, punishment for producing, selling, and possessing child pornography was written into law.

❖ The minimum age for a person buying soft porn/erotica, a *Playboy* magazine for instance, is 16 years. The minimum age for buying porn or entering an adult video store where hardcore pornography is available for rental or sale is 18 years. Violent content, including bestiality, sexual acts involving minors, and violent sexual acts is, of course, legally forbidden in Austria.

❖ Punishment is limited to those who produce or distribute obscene texts, pictures, or films or other obscene objects for profit. Possession or non-commercial exchanges of violent pornography is still permitted.

Resource

▶ Austrian Society For Family Planning Counseling *http://www.oegf.at/*

BELGIUM

BELGIUM

POPULATION: 10,444,268

CAPITAL: BRUSSELS

Major Cities:	Antwerp, Ghent, Charleroi, Liege
Ethnic Groups:	Fleming 58%; Walloon 31%
Languages:	Dutch (official) 60%; French (official) 40%
Major Religions:	Roman Catholic 75%; Protestant, other 25%
GDP per capita (PPP):	$38,500
Urban Population:	97%
Infant Mortality:	4 per 1,000 births
Life Expectancy:	Females: 83 years; Males: 77 years
Adult Literacy:	99%
Health Care System:	3 doctors per 1,000 people

References
- *Reference World Atlas* (2013). NY: DK Publishing.
- *The World Almanac and Book of Facts 2013* (2012) NY: World Almanac Education Group.
- *The World Factbook https://www.cia.gov/library/publications/the-world-factbook/*

Sexual Activity

❖ The age of consent is 16.[1]

❖ About one-third of young women begin having sex before age 18.[2]

Contraception

❖ Almost every woman obtaining an abortion is given a prescription for contraceptives following the procedure.[3]

❖ Contraceptive prevalence in Belgium is high. Results from a study of 1,050 women aged 15–44 showed that 68 percent use a contraceptive method.[3]

❖ Emergency contraception is available over-the-counter.[4]

Abortion

❖ Until April 1990 abortion was illegal in Belgium under all circumstances. However, a small group of health professionals had long provided high-quality abortion services in outpatient facilities and in hospitals.[3]

❖ The 1867 Belgian Penal Code, which defined the pre-1990 abortion law, was based on the Napoleonic Code of 1810, and it restricted abortion under all circumstances.[3]

❖ In April 1990 the Belgian Parliament approved a law that permits abortion within the first 12 weeks of pregnancy when a physician deems the woman to be in a "state of distress"—a condition that is legally undefined.[3]

❖ After 12 weeks of pregnancy, abortion can be performed if two physicians agree that the woman's health is in danger, or in cases of proved fetal malformation.[3]

❖ A six-day waiting period is required from the time of the request to the time of the procedure.[3]

❖ The Belgian legislation does not explicitly require parental consent for minors under the age of 18, but some abortion service providers try to obtain such consent, not differentiating abortion from other medical procedures that require consent.[3]

❖ In 1999, RU-486 (Mifepristone) was approved for marketing in Belgium.[5]

Sex Education

❖ In Belgium, health education and prevention comes under the responsibility of the Communities (French-speaking, Flemish and German-speaking), rather than that of the national state.[6]

❖ In Belgium, "relational and sexuality education" is not particularly linked to a special school subject and it may be part of any subject.[7]

HIV/AIDS[8]

❖ An estimated 20,000 people were living with HIV/AIDS at the end of 2011.

❖ Among Belgian men, gay and bisexual relations are by far the most important transmission path, involving two out of three patients. Among women, heterosexual transmission clearly predominates.

❖ AIDS patients can be divided into two groups: those who have been living in Belgium for a long time and non-residents who were diagnosed shortly after arriving in the country. The profiles of the two groups are quite different. Among residents, mostly Belgian, the male/female ratio is much higher than among non-residents; more than two-thirds of the male residents had homosexual or bisexual contacts. Among the women, heterosexual contacts predominate; this is true also of non-resident patients, whatever their sex.

❖ Most patients live in the cities, especially Brussels, Antwerp and Liège.

LGBT issues

❖ The total ban on same-sex relations was lifted in 1792.[9]
❖ In January 2003 Belgium passed a law similar to The Netherlands allowing same-sex marriage, becoming the second country to legalize same-sex marriage.[9]
❖ Since 2006, couples same-sex couples can adopt and since 2007 transgender people can change their legal gender.[9]
❖ There is no discrimination against gays in the military.[10]

Prostitution[11]

❖ Prostitution is legal. Brothels and pimping are illegal.
❖ One area of concern is the sex trade industry, with many prostitutes who work in Belgium coming from Bulgaria. The penalty for trafficking is 15 years.

Pornography[1]

❖ The legal age for viewing pornography in Belgium is 18 years.
❖ Sex shops and peep shows are tolerated in larger cities.

Resources

▶ Federation of Family Planning Services *http://www.planningfamilial.net/*

▶ Sensoa *http://www.sensoa.be/*

BRAZIL

Major Cities:	Sao Paulo, Rio de Janeiro, Belo Horizonte
Ethnic Groups:	White (Include Portuguese, German, Italian, Spanish, Polish) 54%; Mixed Black and White 38%; Black 6%
Languages:	Portuguese (official); Plus Spanish, English, French
Major Religions:	Roman Catholic 74%, Protestant 15%
GDP per capita (PPP):	$12,100
Urban Population:	87%
Infant Mortality:	20 per 1,000 live births
Life Expectancy:	Females: 77 years; Males: 69 years
Adult Literacy:	7%
Health Care:	Publicly funded clinics and health centers; 2 doctors per 1,000 people

References
- ❑ *Reference World Atlas* (2013). NY: DK Publishing.
- ❑ *The World Almanac and Book of Facts 2013* (2012) NY: World Almanac Education Group.
- ❑ *The World Factbook https://www.cia.gov/library/publications/the-world-factbook/*

Sexual Activity

❖ Age of consent is 14 years old.[1]
❖ Fifty percent of Brazilian teens who become pregnant have their first child by the time they are 16, and one in 10 girls aged between 15–19 has at least two children.[2]
❖ Many young women continue to feel pressured to have sex.[3]

Contraception

❖ In 1979 the advertising of contraceptives was decriminalized and the distribution of contraceptives was permitted.[4]
❖ Currently, 76.6% of Brazilian women in a stable relationship use some form of contraception. Sterilization and the contraceptive pill are the most frequently used methods.[4]
❖ In 1992, 7.5 million women were sterilized during cesarean operations.[4] Brazil passed the Family Planning Law in 1996, which prohibits forcing or requiring anyone to practice family planning as a means of population control.[5]
❖ Emergency contraceptives are available in Brazil in the form of Norlevo/Postinor-2. In 2013 a law was passed to require the "morning-after pill" to be available in health centers.[6]

Abortion

❖ Abortion is illegal except in the case of rape, the life of the mother is in danger or the fetus has severe genetic abnormalities.[7]
❖ Although abortion is outlawed in Brazil except in rare circumstances, the country has one of the highest abortion rates in the developing world. The Health Ministry estimates that 1 in 5 women have had an abortion. Botched abortions are the fourth-leading cause of maternal deaths in Brazil.[7]

❖ Misoprastol is used by some women to induce an abortion. This is an ulcer drug that until 1991 was sold without a prescription.[8]

Sex Education

❖ A poll implemented by the mainstream newspaper in Brazil showed that 86% of the respondents wanted sex education in schools.[9]
❖ One organization known as GTPOS has implemented sexual guidance programs.[9]
❖ There is still a lack of sexuality education, and many teachers do not feel prepared to teach on the topic.[2]
❖ Many parents find talking to their children about sex difficult.[2]

HIV/AIDS[10]

❖ Brazil has one of the highest rates of HIV in the world.
❖ Brazil is home to more than one-third of the total number of people living with HIV in Latin America, with 490,000 people living with HIV/AIDS in 2011.
❖ Estimates of incidence and prevalence were developed for other STI. Of the STI examined, HPV prevalence was highest.

LGBT issues

❖ In 1998, the President of the Brazilian Supreme Court, in a meeting with LGBT activists, came out in support of amending the Constitution to include protection from discrimination on the grounds of sexual orientation, registered partnerships "not constituting matrimony," the end of the ban on lesbians and gays in the military, and protection for people who are transgender.[11]
❖ Brazil's Sao Paulo Gay Pride Parade is thought to be the world's largest gay pride event.[12]
❖ In 2013, Brazil legalized same-sex marriage.[12]

Prostitution

- Prostitution is legal, but it is illegal to operate a brothel, to rent premises to prostitutes, exploit children or live off the earnings of a prostitute.[13]
- Child prostitution is an expanding market in Brazil. There are between 250,000 and 500,000 children involved in the sex trade.[14]
- Some children work in brothels and service 10 to 15 clients a day, and some are sold to ranchers who gang rape them to death.[14]

Pornography[15]

- Legal age for viewing pornography in Brazil is 18 years old.
- The military regime that dominated Brazil from 1964 to 1985 repressed the publication of erotica and sexually explicit films. Since 1985, there has been a great surge in the number of pornography shops and erotic films, videos, and publications.
- Presently both hard- and soft-core pornography are easily accessible in Brazil. Both television and cinema theaters exhibit erotic films.
- Male actors in local movies must wear condoms in penetration scenes. All actors must be 18 or older.
- Scenes showing sex with children or animals are strictly avoided, as is any depiction of sadomasochism, although sexual cruelty and violence may sometimes be shown.

Resources

▶ BEMFAM *http://www.grupobemfam.org .br/bemfam/about_us/*

▶ Brazilian Society for the Study of Human Sexuality *http://www.sbrash.org.br/portal/*

BULGARIA

BULGARIA

POPULATION: 6,981,642

CAPITAL: SOFIA

Major Cities:	Sofia, Ploudiv, Vaina, Burgas
Ethnic Groups:	Bulgarian 77%, Turk 8%, Roman 4%
Languages:	Bulgarian (official)
Major Religions:	Eastern Orthodox 56%, Muslim 7%
GDP per capita (PPP):	$14,500
Urban Population:	73%
Infant Mortality:	16 per 1,000 births
Life Expectancy:	Females: 78 years; Males: 70 years
Adult Literacy:	98%
Health Care:	4 doctors per 1,000 people. During the 1990's Bulgaria began allowing free choice of a family doctor. They began accepting money and medicine from Western countries.

References
❑ *Reference World Atlas* (2013). NY: DK Publishing.
❑ *The World Almanac and Book of Facts 2013* (2012) NY: World Almanac Education Group.
❑ *The World Factbook https://www.cia.gov/library/publications/the-world-factbook/*

Sexual Activity

❖ The age of consent is 14 years old.[1]
❖ Bulgaria ranks among the countries in Europe with the highest birth rates in young teens, indicating the early engagement in sexual activity.[2]

Contraception

❖ There is little opposition from the Orthodox Church regarding the use of contraception and there are adequate supplies on the market, but the lack of use stems from the high price. The cost of one cycle of pills is the same as the cost of an abortion.[3]
❖ There is a low rate of using modern contraceptive methods.[2]
❖ The only emergency contraceptive available in Bulgaria is Postinor; this is a four-pill package given to women who do not have sexual intercourse on a regular basis.[4]

Abortion

❖ The abortion rate in Bulgaria is one of the highest in Europe, only falling behind the Soviet Union and Romania. Abortion exceeded the number of births from the 1980s to early 2000.[2]
❖ According to the law of 1956 every woman has a right to an abortion. This was updated in 1992 allowing abortions up to the 12th week of pregnancy. After the 12th week they are only allowed for a medical condition.[3]
❖ High abortion rates are due to lack of sex education and unavailability of contraceptives.[3]
❖ The religion in Bulgaria which is Eastern Orthodox does not oppose the woman's right to voluntary abortions as other religions in Europe do.[3]

Sex Education[5]

❖ Sexuality education is not mandatory in Bulgaria, and there are no minimum standards for provision.
❖ Since 1996, the Bulgarian Family Planning and Sexual Health Association (BFPA)—the IPPF Member Association in Bulgaria—and the Ministry of Education have used peer education methods to teach sexuality education in and out of schools.
❖ There is little opposition from the Orthodox Church regarding sex education or birth control.

HIV/AIDS[6]

❖ AIDS first appeared in Bulgaria in 1987.
❖ Less than 3,900 people were estimated to be living with HIV/AIDS in 2011.
❖ HIV testing is mandatory among blood donations and systematic among many subgroups of the population. Since 1992 HIV testing is voluntary for pregnant women, STI patients and IDU in treatment centers.
❖ All foreign citizens who enter Bulgaria for more than 3 months must undergo testing.
❖ Diagnosed HIV infected cases are recorded in a national HIV database.

LGBT issues[7]

❖ Discrimination on the basis on sexual orientation is prohibited in areas of social security, health care, social advantages, education, good and services and housing.
❖ Laws on hate and violence do not refer to sexual orientation or gender identity.
❖ LGBT issues have been a target for censorship in Bulgaria, as part of a government campaign for morality in television. For example, in 1995 the Chief of the Bulgarian State Television said that pro-

grams featuring LGBT issues would be taken off the air. In 2013, the Bulgarian Orthodox Church called for the cancellation of the annual gay pride parade.

Prostitution[8]

❖ Prostitution itself is legal, but most activities around it (such as pimping) are outlawed.

❖ A major concern is sex trafficking, since thousands of girls are sent abroad to work as prostitutes, usually against their will.

Pornography[9]

❖ Porn production and distribution is illegal.

❖ Authorities tolerate illegal distribution of hardcore porn in designated shops, and on TV after 11 pm. Softcore material is rarely censored, even by the state TV stations. Magazines and pornographic papers have become increasingly available since the fall of communism in the early 1990s.

Resource

▶ Bulgarian Family Planning and Sexual Health Association *http://www.safesex.bg/en*

CANADA

CANADA

POPULATION: 34,568,211

CAPITAL: **OTTAWA**

Major Cities:	Toronto, Montreal, Vancouver, Ottawa, Edmonton
Ethnic Groups:	British Isles 28%; French 23%; other European 15%; Amerindian 2%; other (Asian, African, Arab) 6%
Languages:	English (official) 59% and French (official) 23%
Major Religions:	Roman Catholic 43%, Protestant 23% (United Church 10%, Anglican 7%, Baptist 2%, Lutheran 2%)
GDP per capita (PPP):	$43,400
Urban Population:	81%
Infant Mortality:	5 per 1,000 births
Life Expectancy:	Females: 84 years; Males: 79 years
Adult Literacy:	99%
Health Care System:	National health care system; 2 doctors per 1,000 people

References
- ❏ *Reference World Atlas* (2013). NY: DK Publishing.
- ❏ *The World Almanac and Book of Facts 2013* (2012) NY: World Almanac Education Group.
- ❏ *The World Factbook https://www.cia.gov/library/publications/the-world-factbook/*

Sexual Activity

* The age of consent is 16 years old.[1]
* Most Canadian youth will have their first experience of sexual intercourse at some point during their teenage years: 30% of 15–17 year olds, 68% of 18–19 year olds.[2]

Contraception

* 74% of sexually active teenagers say they always used contraception in the past six months.[3]
* The most popular methods of birth control include condoms, the Pill (22%), and withdrawal.[3]
* 80% of Canadian women use contraception compared to only 64% of American women.[3]
* Emergency contraception is available without a prescription from a licensed pharmacist. In 2005, Canada's national health agency, Health Canada approved emergency contraception (EC) Plan B for use without a doctor's prescription, allowing the pills to be sold at pharmacies nationwide.[4]

Abortion

* Abortion is considered a safe, legal, insured and funded service, meaning that a woman should not have to pay for abortion services in Canada. Hospital abortions are covered by the national health system.[5]
* Abortion is legal throughout the pregnancy.[5]
* Access is an issue. For example, there are no abortion services in Prince Edward Island.[5]
* Approximately 30% of Canadian women will have at least one abortion in their lifetime.[6]

* The rate of abortion has been declining. From 2001–2012 the abortion rate among teens dropped 24%.[6]
* Medical abortion (more widely known as RU-486) is not legally approved, and importation of that drug into Canada is currently illegal.[7]

Sex Education

* Sex Information and Education Council of Canada (SIECCAN) is the national organization coordinating sexuality education.[8]
* There is strong support for sexuality education in schools; 85% of parents agree that sexuality education should be provided in schools.[9]
* The main reason for Canada's lower teen pregnancy, births, and abortion rates as compared to the U.S. is that Canadian teens of all social classes get comprehensive information about contraception and about how to avoid unwanted pregnancies. They get more sex education in school, and can access high-school-based family planning counseling though the nurse.[10]

HIV/AIDS

* An estimated 71,000 people were living with HIV in Canada at the end of 2011.[11]
* In 2012, Canada released new "Guidelines for HIV Testing" which recommend that primary physicians offer HIV testing as routine health care.[11]
* Nearly half the infections are found in gay men and men who have had sex with men (MSM); women comprise about a quarter of those infected.[11]
* A 2013 study found that 14% of Canadians aged 14 to 59 may be infected with herpes; less than 1% may be infected with Chlamydia.[12]

LGBT issues

❖ The Canadian Human Rights Act forbids discrimination based on sexual orientation by federally-regulated employers, landlords and services. The law applies to the federal government, banks, broadcasters, the phone and telecommunications industry, railways, airlines, and shipping and inter-provincial transportation. Federal constitutional protections are provided by the Canadian Charter of Rights and Freedoms. Provincial human rights laws provide protection based on sexual orientation in all Canadian provinces except Alberta, Newfoundland, and Prince Edward Island.[13]

❖ Canada lifted their ban on gays in the military in October 1992 after a lesbian lieutenant sued the military for discrimination.[14]

❖ In 2003 the provinces of Ontario and British Columbia granted full equal marriage rights to same-sex couples. Same-sex marriage was legalized across Canada by the Civil Marriage Act enacted in 2005 (the 4th country in the world).[15]

❖ In 2013, a bill was introduced to include transgender and gender variant Canadians in the Canadian Human Rights Act and protect them against discrimination. The proposed bill would also prohibit hate speech or the incitement of genocide on the basis of gender identity in the Criminal Code.[16]

Prostitution[17]

❖ Prostitution is legal; however, pimping and public solicitation are illegal.

Pornography

❖ The Canadian criminal law provides that any publication that has as its "dominant characteristic" the "undue exploitation of sex" is obscene. Offenders are usually fined rather than jailed, and the law does not cover those who keep such material for personal use.[18]

❖ In *Butler v. Her Majesty the Queen* (1992) involving the owner of a Manitoba sex shop, the court ruled that although the obscenity law infringed on freedom of expression, it was legitimate to outlaw pornography that was harmful to women. The court also redefined obscenity as sexually explicit material that involves violence or degradation.[19]

❖ Criminal Code 163.1 makes it illegal to possess, produce, distribute or import child pornography (this includes depictions of youths under 18 and those who look as though they are under 18).[20]

❖ In Canada, it is illegal to communicate with a child over the Internet for the purpose of committing a sexual offence against that child (defined as "Internet luring").[20]

Resources

▶ Planned Parenthood Federation of Canada, *http://www.ppfc.ca*

▶ Sex Information and Education Council of Canada (SEICAN) *http://www.sieccan.org/*

CHILE

CHILE

POPULATION: 17,216,945

CAPITAL: SANTIAGO

Major Cities:	Santiago, Concepcion, Vinademeyer
Ethnic Groups:	White and White-Amerindian 95%; Amerindian 3%
Languages:	Spanish (official)
Major Religions:	Roman Catholic 70%, Evangelical 15%
GDP per capita (PPP):	$18,700
Urban Population:	89%
Infant Mortality:	7 per 1,000 births
Life Expectancy:	Females: 81 years; Males: 75 years
Adult Literacy:	96%
Health Care System:	1 doctor per 1,000 people; health care is government responsibility

References
❏ *Reference World Atlas* (2013). NY: DK Publishing.
❏ *The World Almanac and Book of Facts 2013* (2012) NY: World Almanac Education Group.
❏ *The World Factbook https://www.cia.gov/library/publications/the-world-factbook/*

Sexual Activity

❖ Age of consent is 14 in heterosexual relations, 18 in homosexual.[1]
❖ Chile's National Institute for Youth
  reports that almost 14% of Chilean
  women are mothers by the age of 14 and
  an average 40,000 babies are born to
  women younger than age 19 every year.[2]

Contraception[3]

❖ Only a third of women of childbearing
  age use some type of contraceptive
  method.
❖ Contraceptive coverage through the public health care system reaches only 20%
  of women of childbearing age. Other private institutions meet the demand for
  contraceptives for the remaining contraceptive users.[3]
❖ The contraceptives supplied by the public system include oral hormonal contraceptives, intrauterine devices (copper
  T), and to a lesser extent condoms,
  which are provided preferentially to
  high-risk groups. This restricted supply
  limits women's choices in controlling
  their fertility.[3]
❖ Administrative pronouncements state
  that the legal age range for obtaining
  contraceptives is 15 to 44, but in reality
  the public health care system provides
  contraceptives only after the first pregnancy. This retroactive approach limits
  effective access of women of childbearing age to information and services that
  would enable them to exercise their
  reproductive rights.[3]
❖ Women can now opt for voluntary sterilization, which is classified in the
  Responsible Parenthood Norms of the
  Ministry of Health as an irreversible contraceptive method. Women are required
  to meet the following conditions in order
  to be sterilized: they must have four living children, they must be at least 32
  years old, and they must obtain the consent of their partner.[3]
❖ Emergency Contraception has been in a
  battle since 2002. Once available to
  teens over 14, it was overturned, and
  then in 2006 it was available again without parental consent. But in 2008, free
  distribution was ruled unconstitutional.
  and it is now only available in emergen-
  cies.[4]

Abortion

❖ Abortion in Chile is illegal without
  exception and considered one of the
  most restrictive in the world. It is a criminal offense, in 1989 the government
  made a law which prohibits abortion.[3]
❖ Anyone who performs an abortion may
  receive 3 years in prison.[3]
❖ Any woman inducing her own miscar-
  riage may go to prison for 5 years.[3]
❖ It is estimated that approximately
  160,000 abortions are performed each
  year, only some of which result in the
  woman seeking help at a hospital; it is
  also estimated that 35% of pregnancies
  end in abortion and that 40% of the
  women who have abortions are women
  under the age of 18.[2]
❖ Studies also show that one out of every
  three abortions requires hospitalization
  for serious complications, and that complications resulting from abortion repre-
  sent approximately 30% of maternal
  deaths, constituting the primary cause of
  maternal mortality in Chile.[3]

Sex Education[5]

❖ Sex education is minimal and has consisted of a class in biology in the secondary school. Chile has long aligned its views and policies on sex with that of the Catholic Church.

❖ Beginning in 2012, sex education was to be introduced in grades 1st thru 4th, once teachers receive training.

HIV/AIDS[6]

❖ An estimated 51,000 people were living with HIV/AIDS in Chile at the end of 2011.

❖ More than half of the reported AIDS cases are due to men having sex with men and almost 30% were due to heterosexual transmission. Unlike other countries, injecting drug use does not appear to play a large role in HIV transmission in Chile. Heterosexual transmission is increasing in both men and women according to the official figures.

LGBT issues

❖ On December 23, 1998 Chile repealed the section of the law that criminalized same-sex relations between consenting adults. Under the old provision same-sex relations between consenting adults could be punished with up to 5 years' imprisonment at the judge's discretion. The age of consent for same-sex activities was set at 18—higher than that for heterosexual activity—under the new Article 365.[7]

❖ In 2012, anti-discrimination legislation was passed, and in May 2013 over 50,000 people attended a march for gay rights and same-sex marriage.[8]

Prostitution[9]

❖ Prostitution is legal. Much concern centers around human trafficking and child prostituion.

Pornography[10]

❖ In January 2004, Chile amended its Penal Code to strengthen provisions dealing with sexual offenses committed against minors. The newly enacted law adds provisions to the code that prohibit the use of children in pornography and in the sale and distribution of materials containing child pornography, including through electronic means.

Resources

▶ Asociacion Chilena de Proteccion de la Familia (APROFA) *http://www.aprofa.cl/*

▶ International Planned Parenthood Federation-Western Hemisphere Region (IPPF/WHR), 902 Broadway, tenth floor, New York, NY 10010.

▶ Latin American Population Program, Centro de Estudios de Poblacion (CENEP) Casilla 4398, Correo Central, 1000 Buenos Aires

CHINA

CHINA

POPULATION: 1.3 BILLION

CAPITAL: BEIJING

Major Cities:	Shanghai, Peking (Beijing), Tianjin
Ethnic Groups:	Han Chinese 92%, Tibetan, Mongol, Korean, Manchu
Languages:	Standard Chinese or Mandarin (official); Yue, Wu, Hakka, Xiang, Gan, Minbel, Minnan, others
Major Religions:	Daoist (Taoist), Buddhist, Christians, some Muslim
GDP per capita (PPP):	$9,300
Urban Population:	51%
Infant Mortality:	15 per 1,000 live births
Life Expectancy:	Females: 77 years; Males: 73 years
Adult Literacy:	92%
Health Care System:	Three-tier network, made up of county hospitals, township health centers and village health stations, Barefoot Doctors program; 1 doctor per 1,000 people.

References

❏ *Reference World Atlas* (2013). NY: DK Publishing.
❏ *The World Almanac and Book of Facts 2013* (2012) NY: World Almanac Education Group.
❏ *The World Factbook https://www.cia.gov/library/publications/the-world-factbook/*

Sexual Activity

❖ The age of consent is 14 years old.[1]
❖ An increasing number of Chinese adolescents engage in premarital and unprotected sexual activity. As a result, there has been a parallel increase in unwanted pregnancies and abortions, as well as in sexually transmitted infections (STIs).[2]
❖ Sexual activity between men and women not involving intercourse is widely practiced and accepted. Sex was primarily seen for procreation, but women are now looking for sexual fulfillment and pleasure from sex.[3]
❖ In the past 20 years to age of first sex dropped from 22.4 years old to 18.2 years old.[4]
❖ Premarital sex has increased from 15% of women in 1990 to over 50% in 2010.[5]
❖ China is in the midst of a sexual revolution.[5]

Contraception

❖ China has one of the highest rates of contraceptive use in the world with 84.6% prevalence among women who are currently married or in a union.
❖ Intrauterine devices ("IUDs") and sterilization are the most commonly used forms of contraception. Rates of use: 40% for IUDs, 33% for female sterilization.[6]
❖ Women are offered incentives to be sterilized.[7]
❖ The high figures owe much to China's vast network of family planning centers and other government initiatives in local communities that followed the implementation of the One-Child policy in 1979.[6]
❖ Curbing population growth is a national priority. Support for family planning is firmly embedded and codified in national and provincial laws and regulations. Chinese citizens have an obligation to practice family planning.[7]
❖ Emergency contraception is available over the counter and has risen in popularity.[6]

Abortion[7]

❖ Abortion is legal and a service provided by the government. It is encouraged as a means of controlling the population.
❖ Sex-selective abortions for nonmedical purposes are strictly prohibited since there is still a preference for male children. Those who are unable to terminate their pregnancies frequently abandon their female children shortly after birth.
❖ There are approximately 26 abortions for every 1,000 births.
❖ Medication abortion (RU486) was approved for use in 1988.
❖ Official number of abortions performed annually in China is 8 million.
❖ China's law on Maternal and Infant Health Care requires expectant mothers to undergo prenatal exams and to abort any fetus that shows abnormalities. Because these children neither maintain the family line nor support aging parents, they are considered a "luxury."

Sex Education

❖ China seems to be changing its focus from procreation to pleasure. Books, videos and movies about human sexuality are becoming more available and there is a government awareness of the need to educate young people about their bodies and sexual desire.[3]
❖ Sex education is not mandatory in Chinese curriculum, and talking about sex is often considered taboo in Chinese culture.[8]
❖ The country's lack of sex education has contributed to a high rate of abortions and a growing number of HIV cases.[8]
❖ A 2013 survey found that more than 90 percent of Chinese parents support increased sex education curriculum—especially following a series of high profile child sex abuse cases. Forty percent said their children currently receive no sex education.[8]

HIV/AIDS

❖ HIV/AIDS was first reported in China in 1985.[9]

❖ China, with a fifth of the world's population, reported approximately 740,000 people were living with HIV in 2011.[9]

❖ China has the world's largest population of injecting drug users. They account for almost half (44%) of people living with HIV. Almost one-half of China's injecting drug users share needles and syringes, and one in ten also engage in high-risk sexual behavior.[9]

❖ STIs have been recognized as major public-health problems in China since they re-emerged with the introduction of the open door policy and economic liberalization; they rapidly spread throughout the country from the early 1980s onwards, suggesting that unprotected sex with non-monogamous partners is growing in China.[10]

LGBT issues[11]

❖ LGBT issues had remained a taboo till the "open-door" policy was adopted around 1980. Before then, especially during the Great Cultural Revolution, gays and lesbians were subject to public criticism, sentenced to jail or administrative punishment. Even though gays, lesbians and other sexual minorities are still faced with harassment from the police and repression from the government, pressure of this kind is decreasing. Many gays and lesbians are asking for understanding from their parents and friends, coming out of traditional heterosexual marriages and ultimately, fighting for and defending their rights.[11]

❖ The nineties became the "coming-out" time for gays and lesbians in China. At the same time, the government and the society became more tolerant for sexual minorities.[11]

❖ In 1997, China abolished the crime of "hooliganism," largely used as a pretext for criminalizing homosexual and other undesirable behaviors. It came a full six years before the United States Supreme Court struck down similar state anti-sodomy laws.[12]

❖ In 2001, the Chinese Psychiatric Association removed homosexuality from its list of psychiatric disorders and an update to China's "Exit-Entry Administration Law," allows foreign same-sex couples in Beijing to apply for dependent residence permits as of July 1, 2013.[12]

❖ In China, gender reassignment is still a taboo topic, and gender reassignment surgery can be prohibitively expensive and restricted. The government implemented guidelines in 2008 restricting gender reassignment surgery.[1]

Prostitution[13]

❖ Although prostitution is illegal in China, it is visible and available.

❖ Forced re-education is punishment for prostitutes and Johns, which includes legal and moral education and manual labor in a specified camp. Time spent in these camps ranges from 6 months to two years.

❖ There are concerns about violence, drugs, and STIs. There are fears that prostitution may become the main route of HIV transmission as it has in developing countries such as Thailand and India. Some regions have introduced a policy of 100% condom use, inspired by a similar measure in Thailand.

Pornography

❖ Pornography has been banned since 1949. In 1989, a campaign against pornographic activities and publications was introduced.[14]

❖ The resolution of pornography stipulates the death penalty or life imprisonment for serious cases of smuggling, producing, selling or distribution pornographic materials. In less serious cases, it is simply a fine.[15]

❖ In 2011 China shut down over 60,000 porn sites. China has blocked a number of popular websites and Internet services, including Google's YouTube, Twitter, Flickr and Facebook.[16]

Resources

▶ China Association of Sex Education, Mercy Memorial Foundation, 11F, 171 Roosevelt Road, Section 3, Taipei Taiwan, R.O.C. Tel: 866-2-369-675.

▶ China Sexology Association, Number 38, Xue Yuan Lu, Haidion, Beijing 1000083.

▶ State Family Planning Commission, IEC Dept., 14 Zhichun Road, Haidian District, Beijing 100088.

COSTA RICA

COSTA RICA
POPULATION: 4,695,942

CAPITAL: SAN JOSE

Major Cities:	San Jose, Alajuela, Cartago
Ethnic Groups:	White (including Mestizo) 94%, Black 3%
Languages:	Spanish (official), English
Major Religions:	Roman Catholic 76%, Evangelical 14%, Jehovah's Witness 2%
GDP per capita (PPP):	$12,800
Urban Population:	64%
Infant Mortality:	9 per 1,000 births
Life Expectancy:	Females: 81 years; Males: 75 years
Adult Literacy:	95%
Health Care:	1 doctor per 1,000 people. 80% of the population has access to health services. Only 54% of the population has access to prenatal care.

References
❑ *Reference World Atlas* (2013). NY: DK Publishing.
❑ *The World Almanac and Book of Facts 2013* (2012) NY: World Almanac Education Group.
❑ *The World Factbook https://www.cia.gov/library/publications/the-world-factbook/*

Sexual Activity

❖ The age of consent is 18 years old.[1]
❖ 59% of unmarried women ages 15–24 who became pregnant reported that the pregnancy was unintended.[2]
❖ The median age of first intercourse is 19.4 years for women and 17.4 years of age for men.[3]

Contraception

❖ 70% of women use some form of contraception.[4]
❖ More than three-quarters (77%) of women users of modern contraceptive methods acquire them, almost free of charge, from the government public services including the social security system, the Ministry of Health and company physicians. 28% of women use modern methods of contraception, 21% are sterilized and 16% use barrier methods. In metropolitan San José 61% of women users obtain their contraceptives in public health facilities, while 87% of women living in rural areas depend on this source.[5]
❖ Emergency contraception is not available in Costa Rica.[6]

Abortion[7]

❖ Abortion is legal only when maternal health is compromised.

Sex Education[8]

❖ Since August of 1998, the First Lady of Costa Rica was promoting the implementation of a national program of sex education for children and youth which would conform to "Christian values," (meaning it would not include discussions of such topics as gender, homosexuality, and contraception).

HIV/AIDS[9]

❖ An estimated 8,800 people were living with HIV/AIDS in Costa Rica at the end of 2011.
❖ The main mode of HIV transmission is men having sex with men which represents 68% of all AIDS reported cases in the country.

LGBT issues

❖ In a first of its kind decision, Costa Rica's "Defensoria de los Habitantes" [the government's human rights ombudsperson] has ruled that the Costa Rican government may not deny legal recognition to gays and other minorities. The "Registro Civil" of the government here considers applications for all legal charters. In the decision the Defensoria ruled that the original decision by the Registro Civil to deny legal recognition of Triangulo Rosa gay group, is in violation of the country's constitution which guarantees the right of association to all citizens. Decisions made by the Defensoria are legally binding.[10]
❖ In July 2013, legislation was passed (some say "by accident") granting the benefits of domestic partnerships "without discrimination contrary to human dignity." Lawmakers indicated during debate that the changes would open civil unions to same-sex couples, making Costa Rica the first country in Central America to do so.[11]

Prostitution[12]

❖ Prostitution is legal in Costa Rica.
❖ Prostitutes must have an ID card and carry it at all times to prove it.
❖ Age of consent is 18.

Pornography

❖ No information found.

Resources

▶ Asociacion Demografica Costarricense (ADC) *http://www.adc-cr.org/*

▶ Programa Salud Reproductiva, Apartado 1434-1011 Y-Griega, San Jose, Costa Rica.

CUBA

CUBA
POPULATION: 11,061,888

CAPITAL: **HAVANA**

Major Cities:	Havana, Santiago, Camaguey
Ethnic Groups:	Mulatto 51%, White 37%, Black 11%
Languages:	Spanish (official)
Major Religions:	Roman Catholic 85% prior to Castro
GDP per capita (PPP):	$10,200
Urban Population:	75%
Infant Mortality:	5 per 1,000 births
Life Expectancy:	Females: 80 years; Males: 76 years
Adult Literacy:	99%
Health Care System:	6 doctors per 1,000 people

References
❏ *Reference World Atlas* (2013). NY: DK Publishing.
❏ *The World Almanac and Book of Facts 2013* (2012). NY: World Almanac Education Group.
❏ *The World Factbook https://www.cia.gov/library/publications/the-world-factbook/*

Sexual Activity[1]

❖ The legal age of consent is 16 years old.

Contraception[2]

❖ Birth control is free and available to all. Condoms are easy to purchase.

❖ Cuba has sought to expand the range of methods available beyond the IUD, which has long been the predominant method, and to improve the quality of family planning services.

❖ Cuba's family planning policy is implemented through education on the need to limit the number of children to two.

Abortion[3]

❖ Abortion has been legal in Cuba since the late 1960s.

❖ The pregnant woman must be examined by a gynecologist and must receive counseling from a social worker.

❖ If the woman is unmarried and under 16 years of age, parental permission is required.

❖ If gestation is greater than 10 weeks, authorization by health authorities is required.

❖ The abortion must be performed by a physician in an official health center.

❖ Cuba has one of the highest rates of abortion for a developing country (57 per 1,000 women)

Sex Education

❖ The Cuban National Center for Sex Education is a government-funded body whose aim is to develop a culture of sexuality that is "full, pleasurable and responsible, as well as to promote the full exercise of sexual rights."[4]

❖ There is a push to adopt the "Dutch approach" to sex education.[5]

HIV/AIDS

❖ Cuba has one of the world's smallest HIV/AIDS epidemics. An estimated 14,000 people were living with HIV/AIDS in Cuba at the end of 2011.[6]

❖ The country's prevention of mother-to-child transmission of HIV program is among the most effective in the world and has kept the total number of babies born with HIV to date below 100.[6]

❖ Until 1993, Cuba quarantined for life anyone carrying the HIV virus.[7]

❖ Cuba has free universal basic health care; it has high rates of H.I.V. testing; condoms are freely and widely available, concentrating efforts on high-risk groups like prostitutes; it gives its teenagers safe-sex education; it traces the sexual contacts of each person who tests positive.[7]

LGBT issues

❖ Homosexuality has been decriminalized in Cuba since the 1990s. No one can be arrested or brought to trial on grounds of their sexual orientation or gender of identity.[8]

❖ In 2008, a law was passed to allow transgender people to receive sex reassignment surgery and change their legal name. The surgery is available without charge.[4]

Prostitution[9]

❖ Prostitution is illegal in Cuba, however the 40% rise in tourism in Cuba has spawned a resurgence of the nation's sex industry.

Pornography

❖ No information found.

Resources

▶ Centro Iberoamericano de Formacano Pedagogica y Orintacion Educational (CIF-POE), Calle 108. Number 29E08, entre 29 E y 29 F, Ciudad Escolar Libertad, Mariano, La Havana.

▶ Sociedad Cinetifica Cubana Para el Desarrollo de la Familia (SOCUDEF), 5ta Avenida 3207, Esquina 34, Miramar, Havana, Cuba

CZECH REPUBLIC

CZECH REPUBLIC

POPULATION: 10,162,921

CAPITAL: PRAGUE (PRAHA)

Major Cities:	Brno, Ostrava, Pilsen
Ethnic Groups:	Czech 64%, Moravian 5%, Slovak 2%
Languages:	Czech
Major Religions:	Roman Catholic 10%, Protestant 1%, 34% no religion, 45% undeclared
GDP per capita (PPP):	$27,600
Urban Population:	73%
Infant Mortality:	4 per 1,000 births
Life Expectancy:	Females: 81 years, Males: 74 years
Adult Literacy:	99%
Health Care System:	Private practice encouraged, good insurance system, all activities directed by the Minister of Health, with attention to prevention. 4 doctors per 1,000 people.

References

❑ *Reference World Atlas* (2013). NY: DK Publishing.

❑ *The World Almanac and Book of Facts 2013* (2012). NY: World Almanac Education Group.

❑ *The World Factbook https://www.cia.gov/library/publications/the-world-factbook/*

Sexual Activity

- Age of consent for sexual activity is 15.[1]
- Since 1989 the Czech Republic has been experiencing a sexual revolution, development of a sex industry, and societal tendencies toward increased sexual activity.[2]

Contraception

- Until 1990, condoms were the only contraceptives that had to be paid for.[3]
- Contraception is now widely available and use is high.[3]
- Emergency contraception is marketed under the name Postinor 2, and in 2011 became available over-the-counter.[4]

Abortion[3]

- Abortion is available on request, with the consent of the woman and authorization by her gynecologist. After 12 weeks, abortion may be performed for medical reasons only.
- Women under the age of 16 must have parental/guardian consent.
- Health insurance does not cover the cost of an abortion unless it is to save the life of the woman.
- Mifepristone (also known as RU-486 or the "abortion pill") is not legal in the Czech Republic.
- With the advent of widespread contraception and sex education, the post-Communism Czech Republic has seen a sharp decline in the rate of abortion. The number of abortions is lower than any other country in the former Eastern bloc.

Sex Education[5]

- One of the priorities of the Czech Family Planning Association is to make sex education more effective.

- Until 1989, sex education was mainly taught as a part of biology, health or other science classes. Today it is much more comprehensive.
- Sex education is mandatory.
- The Family Planning Association is the main agency involved with sex education. It provides teacher training, youth lectures, and it belongs to a sex education policy-making body, and provides advocacy.

HIV/AIDS[6]

- An estimated 2,100 people were living with HIV/AIDS in the Czech Republic in 2011.
- It ranks among the lowest in Europe and the HIV epidemic is described as "low and slow."
- There is mandatory testing of pregnant women.
- Most infections have been found in men who have sex with men.

LGBT issues[7]

- Consensual same-sex behavior between adults was decriminalized in 1962.
- SOHO is the Czech abbreviation for their Association of Homosexual Citizen's Organizations, made up of about 20 organizations. Since 1995, SOHO has worked towards official registered same-sex partnerships in the Czech Republic, which became legal in 2006.
- The Czech Republic is considered one of the most liberal countries in Central Europe.

Prostitution

- Prostitution is not illegal.[8]
- In 2013, Prague passed a bill regulating prostitution; prostitutes would have to apply for a license and pay taxes.[9]

Pornography

❖ Since the fall of communism in 1989, Czech media lifted its ban on censorship, and pornography began to flourish.[10]

❖ Foreign publications, such as *Penthouse* and *Playboy* are popular, as well as those of the Czech Republic.[11]

Resources

▶ Czech Republic Family Planning Association: Spolecnost pro plánování rodiny a sexuální výchovu (SPRSV), Senovazna 2, 111 21 Prague 1, Czech Republic. Tel: +420 (2) 242 315 24.

▶ Czechoslavak Sexological Society/Institute of Sexology, Charles University, Prague, Karlov Nam_sti 32, Prague 2, 120 00.

DENMARK

Major Cities:	Copenhagen, Arhus, Odense, Aalborg
Ethnic Groups:	Scandinavian, Inuit, Faroese, German, Turkish
Languages:	Danish, Faroese, Greenlandic
Major Religions:	Evangelical Lutheran 95%, other Protestant and Roman Catholic 3%
GDP per capita (PPP):	$38,300
Urban Population:	87%
Infant Mortality:	4 per 1,000 births
Life Expectancy:	Females: 81 years; Males: 77 years
Adult Literacy:	99%
Health Care System:	Doctors appointed by Health Security Service; few private clinics, mostly hospitals. 3 doctors per 1,000 people.

References
- ❑ *Reference World Atlas* (2013). NY: DK Publishing.
- ❑ *The World Almanac and Book of Facts 2013* (2012). NY: World Almanac Education Group.
- ❑ *The World Factbook https://www.cia.gov/library/publications/the-world-factbook/*

Sexual Activity

* The legal age of consent is 15 years old.[1]
* Denmark has a very liberal attitude towards teenage sexuality and has recognized the fact that young, unmarried men and women have a sexual life.[2]

Contraception

* Parental consent is not needed for young people to acquire contraceptives. Denmark was the first country in the world to grant this right to youth in 1966.[2]
* Oral contraceptives, IUDs, and condoms are used most often. Birth control use is high.[3]
* Emergency contraception is available at the pharmacy to anyone over 14.[4]

Abortion

* Denmark has had free access to legal abortion since 1973 when a law passed that allowed women to have an abortion on demand during the first 12 weeks of pregnancy after the submission of an application and after being informed of the risks and alternatives. Abortion is available after 12 weeks when authorized by a committee of one social worker and two physicians. They would approve if one of many conditions applied.[5]
* RU 486 (mifepristone) became available in Denmark in 1999.[6]

Sex Education[7]

* Sex and social life education has been a compulsory subject in Danish schools since 1970 but has been a tradition long before then.
* The sex education curriculum focuses on medical and anatomical lessons, psychological and ethical aspects of sexual and couples' relations, love, sexuality, pregnancy, STD's, and abortion, homo-sexuality and knowledge about sexual minorities.
* Since 2007, all colleges of education are required to offer sexuality education courses.

HIV/AIDS[8]

* An estimated 6,100 people were living with HIV/AIDS in Denmark in 2011.
* An anonymous HIV case reporting system was implemented in August 1990. Data collection includes information on risk behavior, previous testing and results and on nationality. The number of HIV tests conducted are reported monthly.
* Chlamydia is the most common STI in Denmark.

LGBT issues

* In 1989 Denmark became the first country in the world to introduce a registered partnership law. The law enabled two persons of the same sex to register their partnership and gave them (with some exceptions) the same rights and responsibilities as a heterosexual married couple.[9]
* Same sex marriage became legal in 2012.[9]
* In 2010, same-sex couples were allowed to adopt.[10]
* Gay and lesbian people are welcome in the armed forces of Denmark.[10]

Prostitution[11]

* Prostitution is not a criminal offense in Denmark. Neither the customer, nor the prostitute is committing an offense.

Pornography[12]

* In 1969 Denmark was the first country in the world to legalize pornography.
* Possession of child pornography is a crime as well as the sale and production of child pornography.

Resources

▶ Danish Association for Clinical Sexology
(DACS), Kuhlausgade 46, DK-2100,
Copenhagen. Tel: 45/392-92399.
Fax: 45/354-57684.

▶ Danish Family Planning Association
http://www.sexogsamfund.dk/

EGYPT

Major Cities:	Cairo, Alexandria, Giza
Ethnic Groups:	Egyptians 98%, Berbers, Nubian, and Bedouins 1%
Languages:	Arabic (official), English, French
Major Religions:	Muslim (mostly Sunni) 90%, Coptic 9%
GDP per capita (PPP):	$6,700
Urban Population:	44%
Infant Mortality:	23 per 1,000 births
Life Expectancy:	Females: 76 years; Males: 71 years
Adult Literacy:	72%
Health Care System:	Free health service provided by government; fee-for-service by private physicians; 2 doctors per 1,000 people.

References

❑ *Reference World Atlas* (2013). NY: DK Publishing.

❑ *The World Almanac and Book of Facts 2013* (2012). NY: World Almanac Education Group.

❑ *The World Factbook https://www.cia.gov/library/publications/the-world-factbook/*

Sexual Activity

- The legal age of consent is 18 for male-female or lesbian; it is illegal for male-male.[1]

- More than 90% of Egyptian girls undergo a surgical "female circumcision" (FC/FGM) to control or prevent sexual intercourse. A decline is expected over the next 15 years.[2]

- In 1994, the Egyptian government pledged at the U.N. Population Conference to outlaw female circumcision entirely. They first issued a decree banning FC/FGM outside of public hospitals and required physicians to discourage parents from having their daughters undergo FC/FGM. If the parents insisted, the procedure was to be carried out by physicians in hospitals.[3]

- In 1995, Dr. Abdel Fattah, the former Minister of Health, issued a decree amending the 1994 policy on FC/FGM. Using the rationale that Egyptian parents had been successfully convinced to eschew the practice of FC/FGM, the 1995 decree banned physicians from performing FC/FGM in public hospitals. However, this decree did not prevent physicians from performing FC/FGM in their private clinics. In 1996 the new Minister of Health, Dr. Ismael Sallam, ended this policy with a decree prohibiting FC/FGM in public hospitals and private clinics, as well as by non-physicians.[3]

- Shortly after the 1996 decree was issued, it was challenged in court by proponents of FC/FGM and by medical professionals concerned that the ban would lead to increased clandestine FC/FGM. The court declared the health minister's decree unconstitutional for infringing upon parliamentary functions and for interfering with the right of physicians to perform surgery. However, in December 1997, the highest court overturned the lower court's ruling and, in response to proponents of FC/FGM who asserted that Islam requires the practice, declared that Islam does not sanction FC/FGM. The court also declared the practice punishable under the Penal Code.[3]

- Other efforts of the Egyptian government to eliminate FC/FGM include educating traditional birth attendants, doctors, and nurses about the dangers of FC/FGM, and developing mass-media public service messages that discourage FC/FGM.[3]

Contraception

- Egyptian Family Planning Association has been providing services since 1958. Egypt is a leader in family planning in the Middle East, a region where contraceptive use is relatively low.[4]

- The birth rate has been rising in the past few years under the Islamic government. For two decades before it was declining when there was a greater focus on contraception and two-child families.[5]

- Emergency contraception is available by prescription as Contraplan or Postinor-2.[6]

Abortion

- Abortion in Egypt is illegal but very common. The Egyptian penal code of 1937 prohibits abortion in all circumstances but under criminal law, abortion is permitted to save the life of the pregnant woman; the husband's consent is required.[7]

- Anyone who induces an abortion is subject to imprisonment.[7]

Sex Education[8]

- Open discussion of sexuality is socially unacceptable. Egypt uses an approach that emphasizes repression rather than education.

- As of 2010, any sexuality related discussions are prohibited in schools.

HIV/AIDS[9]

❖ An estimated 9,500 people were living with HIV/AIDS in Egypt at the end of 2011.

❖ In Egypt, there appears to be a small amount of AIDS awareness. AIDS cases are either rare or covered up; safe sex practices are virtually unknown, and there is an HIV/AIDS stigma.

❖ Access to groups with known behavioral risk for HIV, such as MSM, sex workers, and drug users, is difficult in Egypt due to cultural constraints.

LGBT issues[10]

❖ There is a strong social sanction against an openly gay or lesbian life. While not illegal, it is considered taboo.

❖ There are concerns that with the election of an Islamic president things will get worse.

❖ Egypt has no exclusive military policies regarding homosexual behavior.

Prostitution[11]

❖ Prostitution has been illegal since 1949. The penalty is prison or a fine.

Pornography[12]

❖ No video or record album may be legally sold until it is scrutinized by a government censor to ensure that the work adheres to the countries "specific moral standards."

❖ In 2012 the government banned all pornographic websites.

Resources

▶ Egyptian Family Planning Association
http://www.efpa-eg.net/en/home.php.

FINLAND

Major Cities:	Helsinki, Espoo, Tamere
Ethnic Groups:	Finns 93%; Swedes 6%
Languages:	Finnish (official) 92%, Swedish (official) 6%
Major Religions:	Lutheran Church 83%
GDP per capita (PPP):	$34,900
Urban Population:	85%
Infant Mortality:	3 per 1,000 births
Life Expectancy:	Females: 83 years; Males: 76 years
Adult Literacy:	100%
Health Care System:	3 doctors per 1,000 people

References
- *Reference World Atlas* (2013). NY: DK Publishing.
- *The World Almanac and Book of Facts 2013* (2012). NY: World Almanac Education Group.
- *The World Factbook https://www.cia.gov/library/publications/the-world-factbook/*

Sexual Activity

❖ The age of consent is 16 years old.[1]
❖ Despite widespread sex education in the schools and mass media, there are no signs of increasing sexual activity among adolescents.[2]

Contraception

❖ In 1972 legislation added an entry into force of the Primary Health Care Act. The law ordered that every local municipality must have a health centre which provides primary health care services for its inhabitants, including contraceptive counseling.[2]
❖ A visit to the family planning clinic and the first contraceptive method (for instance oral contraceptives for 3–6 months) are free of charge. The services are funded by local municipalities with the support of government subsidies, the most common being the Family Federation of Finland, which has clinics in most of the larger towns of the country and a youth center in Helsinki.[2]
❖ Emergency contraception has been available since the mid 1980s. It became available to those 15 and older without a prescription in 2002.[3]

Abortion

❖ Abortion is legal on social grounds and must be performed during the first 12 weeks of pregnancy. The law forbids abortion after the 16th week of pregnancy except on medical grounds, in which case there is no limitation, and abortion may be granted up to the 24th week on eugenic grounds.[4]
❖ Minors need consent from parents, and the cost is free of charge if performed in a public hospital.
❖ Finland has the lowest abortion rate of the Nordic countries. Education and access to services have played a major role in reducing unplanned pregnancy.[5]

❖ RU-486 (Mifepristone) was approved for marketing in 1999.[6]

Sex Education[7]

❖ The need for more effective sex education among teenagers was recognized at the preparatory stage of the present abortion law, and sex education was integrated into the curriculum in 1970.
❖ Currently, sex education in Finland begins at an early age. By the age of 16 all adolescents should have learned about both the physiology of reproduction and methods of contraception.
❖ The Finnish program against HIV has one feature which is probably unique in the world; every year since 1987 the national health authorities have mailed an illustrated magazine to all adolescents who will be 16 that year containing information on the prevention of HIV and other STDs, as well as on sexual issues in general. Since 2000, it is sent to 15 year olds. The package also contains a condom and a letter to the parents. Public response to this campaign has been mainly positive, and it is thought to have contributed to the increased knowledge of sexual issues among teenagers.

HIV/AIDS

❖ An estimated 2,900 persons were living with HIV/AIDS at the end of 2011.[8]
❖ Annual incidence of new HIV cases had been relatively low and stable. This is attributed to education and free access to services and treatment.[8]
❖ The low rate of STIs in Finland can be attributed to the high quality of diagnostic and treatment methods, the free or low cost of these services, the guarantee of confidentiality provided by clinics, and a high rate of condom use. Because there is less stigma of having an STI in Finland and treatment is free or low cost, barriers to treatment and greater spread of STIs are also reduced.[9]

LGBT issues[10]

❖ The Finnish Penal Code protects individuals from discrimination based on their sexual orientation and gender identity in terms of public or commercial services or access to public meetings. The law also prohibits discrimination in hiring and working conditions.

❖ In June 1998 the Finnish Parliament swept away the two provisions of the criminal law which still discriminated against lesbians and gays: the age of consent was equalized, and the law banning the "public encouragement or incitement of unchastity between members of the same sex" (Article 20.9.2) was repealed.

❖ Same-sex couples have been treated as common-law couples when the wording of the law allows it. There is no procedure or custom other than marriage whereby a partnership (be it heterosexual or homosexual) can be registered.

Prostitution[11]

❖ Prostitution is legal, but pimping and running a brothel are not.

❖ Obtaining sexual services from a prostitute linked to human trafficking is illegal.

Pornography[12]

❖ Child, violent, and bestiality pornography is banned. Stores are allowed to sell pornography to those 15 years or older, and hardcore pornography can be sold to those 18 years or older.

Resource

▶ Finland Family Planning Association
http://www.vaestoliitto.fi/

FRANCE

FRANCE

POPULATION: 65,951,611

CAPITAL: PARIS

Major Cities:	Paris, Lyon, Marseilles, Lille
Ethnic Groups:	Celtic and Latin, with Teutonic, Slavic, North African, Indochinese, Basque minorities
Languages:	French (official)
Major Religions:	Roman Catholic 83–88%
GDP per capita (PPP):	$36,100
Urban Population:	85%
Infant Mortality Rate:	3 per 1,000 births
Life Expectancy at Birth:	Females: 85 years; Males: 78 years
Literacy:	99%
Health Care System:	National health care available; 4 doctors per 1,000 people.

References

❏ *Reference World Atlas* (2013). NY: DK Publishing.
❏ *The World Almanac and Book of Facts 2013* (2012). NY: World Almanac Education Group.
❏ *The World Factbook https://www.cia.gov/library/publications/the-world-factbook/*

Sexual Activity

❖ The age of consent is 15 years of age.[1]
❖ The typical age of first intercourse is 16–17.[2]

Contraception

❖ In the early 1990s, France cut condom prices to encourage young people to use them.[3]
❖ The proportion of under-18s who give birth has been more than halved in the last 20 years while the average age at first sex has remained stable for many years, as has the abortion rate. This has only been made possible by an increase in contraceptive use.[4]
❖ Emergency contraception is available over-the-counter and is distributed in schools.[5]

Abortion

❖ French Parliament passed a law that legalized abortion in 1979. In 2001, the French National Assembly approved a new law that extends the time in which a mother can have an abortion from 10 to 12 weeks and other changes. The law also removes parental involvement in sexual matters, including removing parental consent in abortion and access to contraceptives. It also criminalized impeding access to abortion.[6]
❖ France requires that each local area have at least one public hospital that offers abortion services.[6]
❖ In 2013, France made abortion free.[7]
❖ RU-486 (Mifepristone) was first introduced in France in 1988. However, the manufacturer Roussel Uclaf decided to suspend marketing after death threats to staff. The French Minister of Health ordered the drug back on the market two days later calling it the "moral property of women."[8]
❖ More than half (56%) of the abortions performed within the approved gesta-tional period (49 days from last menstrual period) are done using Mifepristone.[9]

Sex Education[10]

❖ In 2001, sexuality education was made mandatory on all levels in all schools.
❖ Sex education is comprehensive—covering biology, social and cultural issues.
❖ The FPA is the main agency involved in sex education provisions. The sex education model consists of prevention, teacher training programs, as well as lectures to youth, thus addressing sex education as "Life Education."

HIV/AIDS

❖ An estimated 160,000 people were living in France with HIV in 2011.[11]
❖ About 80% of the reported AIDS cases in France are male, and 20% are female.[11]
❖ Analysis of AIDS cases by transmission category suggest that the majority of early HIV cases were among IDUs. However, more recently there has been a decline in IDU related AIDS cases suggesting that HIV prevention efforts targeted at drug-injectors have been effective.[11]
❖ As early as 1996, the French Roman Catholic bishop approved the use of condoms to help in the prevention of the HIV virus.[12]

LGBT issues

❖ The French Penal Code prohibits discrimination based on "moeurs" (morals, habits, or lifestyles). This includes sexual orientation. The Code of Labor law prohibits discrimination based on sexual orientation in the workplace, including civil service and armed forces positions.[13]
❖ In May, 2013 France legalized same-sex marriage.[14]

Prostitution[16]

- Prostitution is legal.
- Soliciting and procuring is illegal. A prostitute is the only person who can use the money she earns. If she is married and purchases food for the family her husband can be prosecuted as a procurer.

Pornography[16]

- The legal age for viewing pornography in France is age 18.
- Extremely violent or graphic pornography is considered X-rated, may be shown only in specific theaters, and may not be displayed to minors. Incurs special taxes on revenue (33% for X-rated movies, 50% for pornographic online services).

Resources

- Association Recherche Sexologique du Sud-Ouest (ARS SO); Bordeauz Rive Droite, Route Bergerac, F-33370, Fargues-St.-Hilaine, France.
- Fondateur de L'Association Mondiale de Sexology; 72, Quai Louis Bleriot, 75016, Paris France.

- Syndicat National des Medecins Sexologues (SNMS); 77 Rue Lakana, IF-37000, Tours, France.
- Mouvement Francais pour le Planning Familial (MFPF) *http://www.planning-familial.org/*

GERMANY

GERMANY
(FEDERAL REPUBLIC OF GERMANY)
POPULATION: 81,147,265

CAPITAL: BERLIN

Major Cities:	Berlin, Hamburg, Munich, Cologne
Ethnic Groups:	German 92%; Turkish 2%
Languages:	German (official)
Major Religions:	Protestant 34%, Roman Catholic 34%, Muslim 4%
GDP per capita (PPP):	$39,700
Urban Population:	74%
Infant Mortality:	4 per 1,000 live births
Life Expectancy:	Females: 83 years; Males: 78 years
Adult Literacy:	99%
Health Care System:	Socialized system; 4 doctors per 1,000 people.

References
☐ *Reference World Atlas* (2013). NY: DK Publishing.
☐ *The World Almanac and Book of Facts 2013* (2012). NY: World Almanac Education Group.
☐ *The World Factbook https://www.cia.gov/library/publications/the-world-factbook/*

Sexual Activity

- The legal age for consent is 14.[1]
- The typical age of first intercourse is 16–17.[2]

Contraception

- Many teens (63%) report using contraception in their most recent sexual encounter (compared to only 20% of US teens).[2]
- Over 80% of women who report using contraception say they are on the pill.[3]
- Emergency contraception is available only by prescription. It is free for those under 18.[4]
- In 2013, German bishops approved the use of emergency contraception in cases of rape.[5]

Abortion

- In 1995, in order to reconcile the abortion laws of the former East and West German republics, Germany adopted a law broadening the circumstances under which abortion is permitted in what was West Germany, while increasing the restrictions on abortion in the former East Germany. Under the new law, abortion cannot be prosecuted during the first 14 weeks of pregnancy and is available without limitation as to reason. But, women seeking abortions must meet several procedural requirements, and most abortions are no longer covered by national health insurance.[6]
- An abortion may only be performed after a 3 day waiting period.[6]
- In 1999, RU-486 (Mifepristone) was approved for marketing in Germany.[7]

Sex Education[8]

- The Pregnancy and Family Support Act of 1992 makes it the duty of the Federal and Laender governments to improve sex education.

- Sexuality education is mandatory in all schools.
- Pro Familia, Germany's family planning association, provides sex education in and out of schools, as well as teacher training.

HIV/AIDS

- An estimated 73,000 people were living with HIV/AIDS in Germany at the end of 2011.[9]
- Most of those infected are men who have sex with men.[9]
- Since 2007, Germany has seen a decrease in infections. Much of their success is attributed to prejudice-free education, access to testing, and treatment.[9]
- Germany's gonorrhea rate is 25 times lower than the US.[2]

LGBT issues

- A minimum of 10,000 gay men were forced by the Nazis to wear pink triangles and be confined to concentration camps during World War II.[10]
- In 1993, Berlin included sexual orientation as a non-discrimination criteria in its constitution.[11]
- In 2001, registered partnerships were recognized. Same-sex couples have a status comparable to marriage. However, adoption and child custody rights are withheld.[11]
- Gays cannot be excluded from military service, but homosexual relations between military personnel on duty is illegal.[11]
- In November 2013, Germany will offer a "third gender" option on birth certificates specifically for those children who are born with indeterminate gender. Parents will no longer have to categorize their newborn as "male" or "female." Instead, parents can choose to leave the space blank on their child's birth certificate.[12]

Prostitution

❖ Prostitution is legal in Germany. Communities can limit areas used and the times of day prostitutes work.[13]

❖ Prostitutes must be registered with the health authorities.[13]

❖ Pimping and promoting prostitution are illegal.[13]

❖ EROS Centers can be found where prostitutes rent a room and sit in the window to lure customers.[13]

❖ In 2002, the government changed the law in an effort to improve the legal situation of prostitutes. However, the social stigmatization of prostitutes persists, forcing most prostitutes to lead a double life. Authorities consider the common exploitation of women from Eastern Europe to be the main problem associated with the occupation, as it is estimated that two-thirds of Germany's 400,000 prostitutes come from overseas.[14]

Pornography[15]

❖ All forms of sexual, pornographic, and/or obscene material are easily available in Germany, the soft variety from newsstands and television, the harder types in numerous shops where even the most extreme examples are available under the counter.

❖ Child pornography is banned. Although law defines a child to be a person up to the age of 14, no pornographic material may involve persons below the age of 18. Hard pornography (violence and animal related) may not be produced or distributed; possession is allowed. Hardcore pornography is restricted to buyers of 18 years or older. If a store is accessible to minors, the material must not be on display and may only be sold discreetly and by request. Special parental privilege needed to show hardcore pornography to their children for educational purposes. The law defines pornography to be hardcore pornography, thus anything else is not restricted.

Resources

▶ Pro Familia *http://www.profamilia.de/topic/ home*

▶ National AIDS Committee (Nationaler AIDS-Beirat—NAB), Federal Ministry for Health, 53108 Bonn, Germany; Tel: (228) 941-3200

▶ German Society for Sexual Research (DGSS) *http://www.sexologie.org/*

GREECE

Major Cities:	Athens, Thessoloniki
Ethnic Groups:	Greek 93%
Languages:	Greek (official) 99%, English, French
Major Religions:	Greek Orthodox 98% (official)
GDP per capita (PPP):	$24,900
Urban Population:	61%
Infant Mortality:	5 per 1,000 births
Life Expectancy:	Females: 83 years; Males: 78 years
Adult Literacy:	96%
Health Care System:	6 doctors per 1,000 people

References
❑ *Reference World Atlas* (2013). NY: DK Publishing.
❑ *The World Almanac and Book of Facts 2013* (2012). NY: World Almanac Education Group.
❑ *The World Factbook https://www.cia.gov/library/publications/the-world-factbook/*

Sexual Activity

❖ The legal age of consent is 15 years of age.[1]

❖ Teen pregnancies have declined in the past 30 years.[2]

❖ A significant proportion of teen pregnancies in Greece are to married teens (80% or more).[2]

Contraception

❖ Until 1980, family planning was illegal in Greece; abortion was mainly used as a form of birth control, and despite being illegal, it was widespread.[3]

❖ Over 60% of women rely on withdrawal as their only contraceptive method.[2]

❖ The pill has been available without a prescription since 1963.[2]

❖ Emergency contraception is not yet available.[2]

Abortion

❖ Until the Second World War, abortion was strictly opposed except on medical grounds. Abortion laws were liberalized in 1978, and again in 1986, allowing a woman to have a free abortion in a public hospital up to the 12th week (later abortions are permitted on various grounds).[3]

❖ Women under 18 must have parental consent.[3]

❖ RU-486 (Mifepristone) was approved for marketing in 1999.[2]

Sex Education[4]

❖ Sexuality education has been mandatory since 1995, however the amount of education appears to be limited.

❖ Although family planning clinics were first established in the early 1980s, they are not currently involved in school sex education per se; they are involved in trying to influence public and political opinion and the training of health workers.

HIV/AIDS[5]

❖ An estimated 11,000 people were living with HIV/AIDS in Greece at the end of 2011. Of these 80% are men and 20% women.

❖ Overall, men who have sex with men and IV drug users (IDU) account for the vast majority of reported HIV cases.

❖ HIV cases are increasing, especially among IDUs. The number of cases increased 15 times from 2010 to 2011.

LGBT issues[6]

❖ Since 2005, discrimination is generally prohibited in the workplace.

❖ A public health law introduced in 1981, and reintroduced in 2012, allows forced testing of gay men for STIs. It has been used by police to harass gays.

❖ Less than 50% support same-sex marriage or adoption.

❖ Same-sex kissing is typically not shown on TV, and some channels have been fined for showing same-sex kissing.

❖ Gays and lesbians are banned from being officers in military service.

Prostitution[7]

❖ Prostitution is legal.

❖ Women must register and attend clinics for regular examinations, in some cases as frequently as every two weeks.

Pornography

❖ Soft pornography is a thriving industry and sold at roadside kiosks.[8]

❖ Hard porn is sold in stores to those over 18.[8]

❖ Many Greek paintings (erotic art) show sexual intercourse, fellatio, orgies, pedophilic behavior and a variety of other sexual behaviors.[9]

Resources

▶ Family Planning Association of Greece, Alkaiou 10, 11528 Athens Greece. Tel: 30 210 77 74 607.

▶ Greek Society of Andrology and Sexology, Chalcocondili 50, Athens.

HUNGARY

HUNGARY

POPULATION: 9,939,470

CAPITAL: **BUDAPEST**

Major Cities:	Budapest, Debrecen, Miskolc
Ethnic Groups:	Hungarian 92%, Roma 2%
Languages:	Hungarian (official) 94%
Major Religions:	Roman Catholic 52%, Calvinist 16%, Lutheran 3%
GDP per capita (PPP):	$18,600
Urban Population:	70%
Infant Mortality:	5 per 1,000 live births
Life Expectancy:	Females: 79 years; Males: 72 years
Adult Literacy:	99%
Health Care System:	Since 1974, 99% of the population was covered and was eligible for free health care. Limited private practice is permitted; 3 doctors per 1,000 people.

References

❑ *Reference World Atlas* (2013). NY: DK Publishing.
❑ *The World Almanac and Book of Facts 2013* (2012). NY: World Almanac Education Group.
❑ *The World Factbook https://www.cia.gov/library/publications/the-world-factbook/*

Sexual Activity

❖ The age of consent for sexual activity is 14.[1]

Contraception

❖ Hungary has achieved a relatively high contraceptive prevalence rate: 77 percent of reproductive-age women use contraception.[2]

❖ Postinor, a form of emergency contraception, was developed in Hungary. It is available with a prescription.[3]

❖ Postinor was originally promoted as the ideal method of contraception for people with infrequent sexual contacts, and it soon became one of the most widely used forms of birth control.[3]

❖ Though there is little national data about such statistics, users of emergency contraception tend to be young, unmarried women, who switch to oral contraception when in a stable relationship, and then to IUDs when their families are completed.[3]

Abortion

❖ Abortion has been available since 1953.[4]

❖ Abortion is available up to 12 weeks, with exceptions made for the following reasons: health risk to mother or fetus, rape or other sexual crime, or due to the crisis situation of the pregnant woman.

❖ Minors must have parental consent.[4]

❖ Counseling is mandatory. Women must wait three days after counseling but must have the abortion within eight days of the counseling.[4]

❖ The "crisis situation" is defined by the woman herself, but is not discussed, as it is considered a private matter.[4]

❖ Legislation in 2012 to recognize life from the moment of conception has raised concerns about the future of legal abortion.[5]

Sex Education[6]

❖ Some sex education subjects exist in school curricula, though it is linked with Biology, Health, or the Natural Sciences.

❖ There is a perception by some that sexuality education teaches "indecent lifestyles."

❖ There is no opportunity for formal sex education training for teachers.

❖ Family Planning Association is the main agency involved in sex education.

HIV/AIDS[7]

❖ An estimated 4,100 people were living with HIV/AIDS in Hungary at the end of 2011. It is among the countries with a low HIV rate.

❖ The majority of reported HIV infections are among men (82%); 25% of cases are from foreign citizens.

❖ Testing is mandatory for blood donors and STI patients.

❖ A national HIV reporting system has existed since 1985.

LGBT issues

❖ In May 1996, Hungary became the first Eastern European country to extend traditional common-law marriage rights to same-sex couples. Gay couples who live together have all the rights of heterosexual spouses—including inheritance and pensions—but are not allowed to adopt children.[8]

❖ Same-sex relations were decriminalized in 1961. The age of consent for same-sex practices was 20 years between 1961 and 1978. In 1978 this was changed to 18 years. Section 199 Penal Code (which referred to homosexuality as "unnatural illicit sexual practices"), whereas the age of consent for heterosexuals is 14 (Section 201 Penal Code). Section 199 Penal Code provides a penalty of up to 3 years' imprisonment for a violation.[9]

Prostitution[10]

❖ Prostitution has been legal since 1992.
❖ Prostitutes may be found in clubs (La Dolce Vita), bars, hotels, and through the newspaper "Expressz" under the headline "Szexpartnert," where you may find agencies and massage parlors.
❖ Prostitutes work legally in certain designated areas—away from schools and churches.

Pornography[11]

❖ Pornography has been legal since the fall of communism in 1989.
❖ Because there were no laws regulating pornography, Hungary became a popular place to produce films.
❖ It is thought that due to the poor economic conditions, performers are more desperate to succeed and therefore will engage in more extreme forms of sexual intercourse. For example, multiple penetration and anal intercourse are much more common in pornography produced in Hungary than in America.

Resources

▶ Family Planning Association of Hungary: Magyar Család- és Növédelmi Tudományos Társaság, Keleti Karoly u. 5)-7, 1024 Budapest Hungary. Tel: 36 (1) 345 67 2.

▶ Pro Familia Hungarian Scientific Society, Buai Laszl u. 2. III. em. 1, 1024 Budapest, Hungary.

INDIA

INDIA

POPULATION: 1.2 BILLION

CAPITAL: NEW DELHI

Major Cities:	Bombay, Calcutta, Delhi, Madras
Ethnic Groups:	Indo-Aryan 72%, Dravidian 25%
Languages:	Hindi (official), English (associate official), 14 regional official languages
Major Religions:	Hindu 81%, Muslim 13%, Christian 2%
GDP per capita (PPP):	$3,900
Urban Population:	31%
Infant Mortality:	45 per 1,000 births
Life Expectancy:	Females: 69 years; Males: 66 years
Adult Literacy:	61%
Health Care System:	Government is responsible for all health care; hospitals; public/private physicians; < 1 doctor per 1,000 people.

References
❑ *Reference World Atlas* (2013). NY: DK Publishing.
❑ *The World Almanac and Book of Facts 2013* (2012). NY: World Almanac Education Group.
❑ *The World Factbook https://www.cia.gov/library/publications/the-world-factbook/*

Sexual Activity

- The legal age of consent is 16 for hetero-sexuals (except Manipur where it is 14); same-sex relations is 18.[1]
- All types of sexual interaction before marriage are forbidden; total self-restraint is still advocated. Even the discussion of sex is taboo but this is slowly weakening.[2]
- The mean age at first coitus: 18 years.[2]

Contraception

- Nearly 50 years ago, India became the first country in the developing world to initiate a state-sponsored family planning program with the goal of lowering fertility and slowing the population growth rate.[3]
- The government of India has been a powerful proponent of population control. India's population policy has been characterized by a drive to reduce fertility rates and to achieve demographic goals. For example, the central government established specific demographic targets to decrease the level of approximately 33 births per 1,000 to the low 20's by the year 2000. Moreover, targets for the numbers of users of specific types of contraception, particularly sterilization and IUDs, are also set.[4]
- Cash incentive programs for the recipients of sterilization and IUD services, the medical providers of such services, and the health workers who "motivate" an individual or couple to become sterilized also exist.[4]
- Since the mid-1970s, the Indian government has promoted sterilization, which many reject because it is irreversible and seen as a human rights violation.[3]
- In 2006, 57% of Indian women used contraception; only 3% used the pill.[6]
- A group of Indian scientists is studying a contraceptive injection for men that they believe will become more popular than the vasectomy because it will be easily reversible.[5]
- Emergency contraception is widely used and is available over-the-counter in several brands: i-pill, Unwanted 72 and Preventol, are readily accessible over-the-counter drugs throughout India.[6]

Abortion

- India is an example of a country where a liberal abortion law does not ensure that women can access safe and legal procedures. India's Medical Termination of Pregnancy Act permits abortion on socio-economic grounds, and even recognizes that the anguish of an unwanted pregnancy resulting from contraceptive failure could constitute a "grave injury to the mental health of the pregnant woman" that could justify an abortion. However, only 1,800 of the 20,000 primary health centers have legally certified abortion facilities. Women with unwanted pregnancies are forced to rely on low-cost procedures, which are often undertaken by untrained practitioners under unsanitary conditions.[7]
- A woman dies in India every two hours because an abortion goes wrong. Each year 19–20 million women risk their lives to undergo unsafe abortions and 20,000 women die.[8]
- Unless a medical emergency exists, a legal abortion must be performed during the first 20 weeks of gestation by a registered physician in a government hospital.[9]
- A legal abortion is free of charge only if it is performed in a government hospital. These hospitals are often inaccessible, therefore the number of illegal and/or unregistered abortions are estimated to around 6 million annually.[9]
- It is estimated that unsafe abortions account for 20% of maternal deaths in India.[9]

- Female feticide is common. In an effort to halt widespread abortions of female fetuses, the Indian Parliament passed a law prohibiting doctors from telling expectant parents of their offspring's gender. The bill also bans the advertisement and performance of ultrasounds solely to determine gender.[10]
- Mifepristone/RU 486 (non-surgical "abortion pill"): is registered for use in India.[11]

Sex Education[12]

- There has been little to no sex education at any level. A 1999 attempt to launch a sexuality education program was unsuccessful.
- Sex education has not been taught in schools because of the fear that it "would ignite the curiosity of students about experimentation, resulting in teenage pregnancies and promiscuity." Note: 1 in 6 girls in India become pregnant and give birth; of 16 million teen girls giving birth each year, 4 million are in India.
- The Ministry of Health and Family Welfare began coordinating primary and adult education programs and is promoting its family planning agenda in rural areas.

HIV/AIDS

- An estimated 2.4 million people were living with HIV/AIDS in India at the end of 2013—more than any other country in the world except South Africa.[13]
- The first case of AIDS in India was detected in 1986. Since then, HIV infections have been reported in all States and Union Territories.[13]
- With a population of one billion—about half in the 15–49 year-old population—HIV epidemics in India will have a major impact on the overall spread of HIV in Asia and the Pacific, as well as globally. India accounts for half of all HIV cases in Asia.[14]

- The spread of HIV within India is as diverse as the societal patterns between its different regions, states and metropolitan areas. The epidemics are focused very sharply in a few southern States, with most of India having extremely low rates of infection.[12]
- An overwhelming majority of the total reported national AIDS cases—96%—were reported by only 10 of the 31 states. The major impact is being felt in Maharashtra in the west, Tamil Nadu in the south with adjacent Pondicherry, and Manipur in the northeast.[12]
- Most HIV infections in India (more than 80% of reported AIDS cases) are due to unprotected heterosexual intercourse. Injecting drug use is the main driver of the HIV epidemics in the north-east, and there is a substantial overlap between injecting drug use and paid sex in some parts of the country.[13]
- India has no anti-discrimination law to protect those who are HIV positive. As recently as 2013 the government rejected such a law.[14]

LGBT issues[16]

- In 2009, the New Delhi High Court decriminalized same-sex relations between consenting adults. This overturned Section 377 of the Indian Penal Code which criminalized male to male sex with up to 10 years imprisonment.[16]
- LGBT persons have slowly gained a degree of acceptance in some parts of India, especially its big cities. Many bars have gay nights, and some high-profile Bollywood films have dealt with gay issues. Large gay pride parades have occurred in recent years in New Delhi and other big cities, including Mumbai and Kolkata.[16]
- Despite some progress, being gay remains deeply taboo in most of the country, and many gays and lesbians hide their sexual orientation from friends and relatives.[16]

- In India, transgender people are called "hijras" and were granted voting rights as a third sex in 1994.[17]

Prostitution

- Prostitution is legal, but soliciting and prostitution in a public place is illegal.[18]
- According to health authorities, Bombay has over 100,000 prostitutes.[18]
- More than half are infected with HIV.[18]
- In southwestern India, thousands of people have been dedicating their daughters to a religiously sanctioned life of prostitution for well over a millen-

nium.[19] These girls, as young as 6, are initiated into a life of sexual slavery as servants of the gods.[20]

- Children's advocacy groups like UNICEF estimate that 70,000 to 100,000 children in India are involved in the sex industry.[21]

Pornography[22]

- Pornography is currently legal. The distribution of pornography is illegal.
- In response to the rise in sexual assaults, a bill was introduced in 2013 seeking to make it illegal to view.

Resources

▶ Family Planning Association of India (FPAI) http://www.fpaindia.org/

▶ Indian Association of Sex Educators, Counselors, and Therapists (IASECT), 203 Sukhsagar, N. S. Patkar Marg., Bombay 400 007. Tel: 91-22/361-2027.

IRAN

IRAN

POPULATION: 79,853,900

CAPITAL: TEHRAN

Major Cities:	Tehran, Esfahan, Mashhad
Ethnic Groups:	Persian 61%, Azeri 16%, Kurd 10%
Languages:	Persian 53%, Turkic 18%, Kurdish 10%, Gilski and Mazandarani 7%
Major Religions:	Shi'a Muslim 89%; Sunni Muslim 9%
GDP per capita (PPP):	$13,300
Urban Population:	69%
Infant Mortality:	40 per 1,000 births
Life Expectancy:	Females: 72 years; Males: 69 years
Adult Literacy:	77%
Health Care System:	< 1 doctor per 1,000 people

References

❑ *Reference World Atlas* (2013). NY: DK Publishing.

❑ *The World Almanac and Book of Facts 2013* (2012). NY: World Almanac Education Group.

❑ *The World Factbook https://www.cia.gov/library/publications/the-world-factbook/*

Sexual Activity

* There is no age of consent to heterosexual sexual activity outside of marriage; the couple must be married to have sex. It is illegal for same-sex relations.[1]
* Polygyny is regulated by Islamic custom, which permits a man to have as many as four wives simultaneously, provided that he treats them equally.[2]
* Pre-marital and extra-marital sex is illegal in Iran. In certain cases involving women, punishment can include execution.[3]
* On May 16th 1993 the Iranian Parliament ratified a bill aimed at encouraging couples to have no more than three children. Legislation will grant special government benefits to the first three children only. This rule took affect in 1994.[4]
* According to Amnesty International—a 16-year-old girl was publicly hanged in Iran in August 2004 for alleged "acts incompatible with chastity" and in another case, a teenage girl with a mental age of eight is facing the death penalty for commercial sex work in Iran. Amnesty International refers to reports that say she was repeatedly raped, bore her first child at age nine and was passed from pimp to pimp before having another three children. Women around the world are regularly murdered, assaulted, beaten, stoned, mutilated and have acid thrown at them—all in the name of "honor." Honor crimes are premeditated attacks carried out by family members as punishment for deeds they believe have dishonored the family name. The victims of these crimes are overwhelmingly female.[5]

Contraception

* The goal of the Social and Cultural Development Plan is to reduce the total fertility rate to four children per woman.[6]

* The Government has proposed to raise levels of contraception use to 24% of women of childbearing age and to prevent 1 million unwanted births.[6]
* The Health Ministry distributes condoms, IUDs and birth control pills for free. Vasectomies are also free.[7]
* Iran is the only country in the world that requires both men and women to take a class on modern contraception before receiving a marriage license.[8]

Abortion

* In 1973, induced abortion was legalized in Iran. However, after the revolution in 1979, abortion was made illegal on most grounds.[6]
* In 2005, Iran's law changed to permit abortion during the first four months if the fetus is mentally or physically handicapped or if the mother's life is in danger. According to the new law, the woman's consent is sufficient to carry out the abortion.[9]

Sex Education

* In order to get a marriage license, couples must take a segregated course in family planning.[6]
* Iran's sexuality education programs are employing more comprehensive, age-appropriate educational materials, explicit premarital counseling, and male education. They are seen as more progressive than the U.S.[10]

HIV/AIDS

* An estimated 96,000 people were living with HIV/AIDS in Iran at the end of 2011.[11]
* The HIV epidemic in the Islamic Republic of Iran appears to be accelerating at an alarming trend. According to reports by the National AIDS Program, the number of newly diagnosed HIV infections and AIDS cases in 2001 shows a three-fold increase in comparison to both years 2000 and 1999.

- Injecting drug use drives the epidemic in Iran. Drug users in Iran are estimated at two million among a population of just over 70 million—per capita, the highest rate in the world. [12]
- There has been a significant increase of total numbers of reported STI cases in the country. Candidiasis, Trichomoniasis, Chlamydia and Gonorrhea are the four main causes, accounting for over 60% of the cases. [11]

LGBT issues

- Same-sex relations are illegal in Iran. [13]
- There are eight countries with the death penalty for homosexuality: Iran is one of them (along with Afghanistan, Mauritania, Pakistan, Saudi Arabia, Sudan, United Arab Emirates and Yemen). [13]
- Sodomy is a crime, for which both partners are punished. The punishment is death if the participants are adults, of sound mind and consenting. A non-adult who engages in consensual sodomy is subject to a punishment of 74 lashes. [14]
- The punishment for lesbianism involving persons who are mature, of sound mind, and consenting, is 100 lashes. If the act is repeated three times and punishment is enforced each time, the death sentence will apply on the fourth occasion. [14]
- According to Amnesty International at least three gay men and two lesbians were killed in January 1990, as a result of the Iranian government's policy of calling for the execution of homosexuals. They were publicly beheaded. [14]

Prostitution

- Prostitution is illegal in Iran. [15]
- On May 6, 1994 an American woman, Mary Jones of Texas was arrested and convicted for prostitution in Iran. She received 80 lashes as her punishment. [16]

Pornography [17]

- Pornography is illegal in Iran.
- The Iranian Parliament has approved legislation providing for capital punishment for producers & distributors of pornographic videotapes.
- The bill that provides a maximum five years prison term and $100,000 in fines for first offenders, said the principal promoters of pornographic videos can receive the death penalty.

Resources

- FPA Iran, No. 2/1, 8 Street Behrooz Street, Mohseni Square Mirdamad Avenue, PO Box 19395-3518, Tehran 19119, Islamic Republic of Iran. Tel.: 9821 222 3944.
- Islamic Women's Institute (13643), No. 1-275 Hedayat St., N. Saddi, Tehran, Islamic Republic of Iran Tel: 98 21 3115656.

IRELAND

Major Cities:	Dublin, Cork
Ethnic Groups:	Irish 87%, English
Languages:	English predominates, Irish (Gaelic) spoken by minority (both official)
Major Religions:	Roman Catholic 87%; Church of Ireland 3%
GDP per capita (PPP):	$42,600
Urban Population:	62%
Infant Mortality:	4 per 1,000 births
Life Expectancy:	Females: 83 years; Males: 78 years
Adult Literacy:	99%
Health Care System:	3 doctors per 1,000 people

References

❑ *Reference World Atlas* (2013). NY: DK Publishing.

❑ *The World Almanac and Book of Facts 2013* (2012). NY: World Almanac Education Group.

❑ *The World Factbook* https://www.cia.gov/library/publications/the-world-factbook/

Sexual Activity[1]

❖ The legal age of consent is 17 years old.

Contraception

❖ Contraception was restricted in the Irish Republic by the Censorship of Publications Act, 1929, and the Criminal Law Amendment Act, 1935 (reformed in 1979). Limited to medical prescription through pharmacies by the Health (Family Planning) Act of 1979, condoms were de-restricted (including vending machines) in June 1993.[2]

❖ State funding of services is restricted to centers providing advice on natural family planning methods. Contraceptives are available from some pharmacies, the condom being the most popular.[3]

❖ Even though Ireland is a highly religious country, with much more conservative values regarding love, sex, and marriage, Roman Catholic adolescents have a relatively positive attitude toward the use of contraception.[4]

❖ Emergency contraception has been available in Ireland since 2011.[5]

Abortion

❖ Abortion is illegal in all circumstances other than when necessary to preserve the pregnant woman's life. In 1967 the Abortion Act was enacted in Britain which stated that abortions may be carried out, as deemed by two doctors, if the life of the mother, mentally or physically, is in danger, or of the infant will suffer serious mental or physical abnormalities or handicap after birth. But in 1983, the Eighth Amendment to the Constitution of the Republic of Ireland was inaugurated, which absolutely made abortion illegal, unless the life of the mother is in danger.[6]

❖ Up until November 1992 it was illegal for counselors to provide information on where one could seek an abortion. Earlier that year, a 14 year-old rape victim was prevented by the High Court from going to Britain to obtain an abortion. This led to a Supreme Court ruling allowing her to obtain an abortion, since her life was in danger due to suicide. Thus, in November, the freedom to travel abroad and obtain information was approved.[7]

❖ In the summer of 2001 Irish pro-choice activists welcomed a visit by the Women on Waves ship, a fully equipped reproductive health care clinic that travels to countries where abortion is illegal. The visit attracted national and international attention to the lack of safe, legal abortion in Ireland. The trip to Ireland was the ship's "maiden visit" and was supported by a group of over 200 Irish volunteers nationwide. Over 6,000 Irish women go to Britain for abortions each year, yet cannot avail themselves of the same service in their home country. Even those women who face life-threatening pregnancies must suffer through many obstacles to obtain abortion services in Ireland. The "Irish solution to the Irish problem"—exporting the abortion issue to Britain—is no solution for women facing a crisis pregnancy. The Women on Waves visit was an enormous success in Ireland. Although complications with the Dutch licensing laws led to a decision not to provide abortions at sea during this visit, volunteers successfully provided abortion information and contraceptive access, including emergency contraceptives, that would otherwise have been unavailable in Ireland. The ship served over 300 women while also drawing international attention to the enormous difficulties created by Ireland's draconian abortion laws.[8]

❖ In 2013, Ireland passed a new law allowing abortion in exceptional cases. The Protection of Life During Pregnancy Act will allow terminations to be carried out where there is a threat to the life of the mother. It will also be allowed where there is medical consensus that the expectant mother will take her own life over her pregnancy.[9]

Sex Education

* Sex education in Ireland is referred to as Relationship and Sexuality Education and falls within the Social Personal and Health Education curriculum. It has been mandatory at the primary and middle school since 2003.[10]
* A 2005 survey by the Crisis Pregnancy Agency reported that much of the sex education is inadequate (too little, too late, and too biological).[10]
* The training program for teachers is entitled, Sense and Sensibility.[10]
* The Irish Family Planning Association (IFPA) provides materials, a telephone hotline, and posters. The aim is to encourage young people's right to enjoy their sexual lives with dignity, respect, and equality; to make free and informed choices, and to make accessible the information and services necessary for young people to enjoy safe and happy sexual lives.[2]

HIV/AIDS[11]

* An estimated 7,800 people were living with HIV/AIDS in Ireland at the end of 2011. The majority (34%) are drug injectors. A further 32% are heterosexual and 22% gay/bi-sexual cases.
* The epidemiology of HIV infection in Ireland has changed considerably in the last decade.
* In recent years the incidence of both new injecting drug use and gay/bi-sexual cases has declined and remained relatively stable, however there have been marked increases in heterosexual cases.

LGBT issues

* In June 1993, despite strong opposition of the Roman Catholic Church, same-sex relations between consenting males was made legal. The age of consent was set at 17, the same age for heterosexuals.[12]
* In 1989 the Prohibition of Incitement to Hatred Act was enacted, making it illegal to incite hatred against lesbians and gay men.[12]
* The Unfair Dismissals (Amendment) Act 1993 provides that dismissal on the grounds of an employee's sexual orientation will automatically be deemed unfair.[13]
* In 2010, Ireland passed the Civil Partnership Act recognizing same-sex unions.[13]
* Ireland will be putting same-sex marriage to a vote in 2014.[13]
* The rights of transgender people are gradually being recognized in Irish law. For example, the Passports Act 2008 saw the first statutory recognition of transgender people in providing for a person's right to apply to have a passport issued in their new gender.[14]

Prostitution[15]

* Prostitution is legal. However, due to concerns about the link to organized crime, 2013 legislation was introduced to criminalize those who purchase sex rather than the prostitute. This is referred to as the Swedish model, which focuses on arresting the men who use prostitutes. The bill is being debated.

Pornography[16]

* Pornography is legal, although the Roman Catholic Church has lobbied to make it illegal for all.

Resource

▶ Irish Family Planning Association (IFPA), *http://www.ifpa.ie/*

ISRAEL

ISRAEL

POPULATION: 7,353,985

CAPITAL: JERUSALEM

Major Cities:	Jerusalem, Tel Aviv-Yafo, Haifa
Ethnic Groups:	Jewish 76%, non-Jewish (mostly Arab) 20%
Languages:	Hebrew (official) and Arabic (used officially for Arab minority), English
Religions:	Judaism 76%, Muslim 17%, Christian 2%
GDP per capita (PPP):	$28,400
Urban Population:	92%
Infant Mortality:	4 per 1,000 births
Life Expectancy:	Females: 83 years; Males: 79 years
Literacy:	97%
Health Care System:	Publicly funded health centers/clinics; 4 doctors per 1,000 people

References
- *Reference World Atlas* (2013). NY: DK Publishing.
- *The World Almanac and Book of Facts 2013* (2012). NY: World Almanac Education Group.
- *The World Factbook https://www.cia.gov/library/publications/the-world-factbook/*

Sexual Activity[1]

❖ The legal age of consent is 16 years old.

Contraception[2]

❖ Modern contraception is widely available. Two studies among Israeli Jews found that they relied heavily on the IUD as a form of contraceptive. Sterilization was little used and withdrawal, although in decline, was still relied on to a significant extent.[2]

❖ The "morning after" pill, Postinor 2, became available over–the-counter in 2002.[3]

Abortion

❖ Abortion has been allowed since 1952.[4]

❖ An abortion must be performed by a physician in a recognized medical institution, with the written consent of the pregnant woman. A legal abortion requires the approval of a committee made up of two physicians and a social worker. The committee members must be appointed by the director of the hospital where the abortion will be performed, or by the Minister of Health or a person appointed by him if the procedure is to be performed in another recognized medical institution.[4]

❖ Abortions performed for medical reasons are paid for by the government, as well as for any reason if the woman is under 18; the woman pays for abortions performed on other grounds.[4]

❖ RU-486 (Mifepristone) was approved for marketing in 1999.[5]

Sex Education

❖ Sex education is relatively new in Israel. It has grown from a sporadic, peripheral activity to a recognized and acceptable subject.[6]

❖ However, a 2007 study found that 86% of students did not feel they received adequate sex education and their knowledge of the subject was lacking.[7]

❖ Israel family Planning Association is run from the center of Tel Aviv. It provides training on sex education and family planning. The Association hosts an information resource center with books, journals, videos and they also produce their own educational materials in Hebrew and Russian. They also run special educational projects on HIV/AIDS and safer sex.[2]

HIV/AIDS[8]

❖ An estimated 8,500 people were living with HIV/AIDS in Israel at the end of 2011.

❖ Since the mid-90's there has been a slight but steady increase in new HIV cases detected annually in Israel. More cases are found amongst IDUs and men who have sex with men, and among new immigrants.

❖ An HIV/AIDS registry has existed since the beginning of the epidemic. HIV testing is systematic among blood donors and prisoners and among select groups of immigrants from HIV-hyper-endemic countries. Testing is confidential and free of charge for any person requesting the service.

❖ Testing is done at all community clinics, all across the country.

❖ Health education programs are developed for both the general population and for groups with risk behaviors. Treatment and follow-up are specialized in regionally distributed AIDS centers, which can provide adequate follow-up and ART treatment to all adherent patients.

LGBT issues

❖ Israel's Knesset has passed a law prohibiting employers from discriminating against employees and job applicants because of sexual orientation.[9]

❖ Until 1988 male homosexuality was punishable under Section 351 of the Penal Code, with up to ten years' imprisonment, although there was already a policy of non-prosecution. In that year Section 351 was repealed by the Knesset.[10]

- In 1994, same-sex partnerships became recognized.[10]
- Tel Aviv, whose annual Gay pride parade attracts more than 100,000 people, was voted "Best of Gay Cities 2011" in an American Airlines survey.[11]

Prostitution[12]

- Prostitution is legal in Israel. What is illegal is a second party making money off of this practice (i.e. pimping, brothel owner)

- Renting an apartment to a working girl is illegal because the rent is money made from prostitution.

Pornography[13]

- Pornography in Israel is legal.
- Pornography is banned from television, and recent proposed legislation is being considered for banning pornographic websites.

Resources

▶ Institute for Sex Therapy. Sheba Medical Center, Tel Hashomer.
▶ Israel Family Planning Association
  http://www.euromedalex.org/node/4108

▶ Ministry of Education & Culture. Psychological and Counseling Services, 2 Devorah Hanevia Street, Jerusalem.

ITALY

Major Cities:	Milan, Naples, Rome, Turin
Ethnic Groups:	Italian, small ethnic minorities of German, French, Slovene, Albanian
Languages:	Italian (official), German, French, Slovene
Major Religions:	Christian 80% (mostly Roman Catholic)
Annual Income per Person	$30,600
Urban Population:	68%
Infant Mortality:	3 per 1000 births
Life Expectancy:	Females: 85 years; Males: 79 years
Adult Literacy:	98%
Health Care System:	National health plan, private hospitals; 4 doctors per 1,000 people.

References
- ❑ *Reference World Atlas* (2013). NY: DK Publishing.
- ❑ *The World Almanac and Book of Facts 2013* (2012). NY: World Almanac Education Group.
- ❑ *The World Factbook https://www.cia.gov/library/publications/the-world-factbook/*

Sexual Activity

❖ The age of consent in Italy is 14 years old.[1]

Contraception

❖ Contraceptive use was legalized in 1971. Prior to that time, contraceptives were allowed only for medical reasons, though transgressions were tolerated.[2]

❖ According to Italian law, doctors are free to follow their faith and refuse to provide contraception. Nearly 75% of doctors are conscientious objectors.[3]

❖ There has been a concern among legislators that induced abortion would become a method of family planning. Nevertheless, it has been mainly used as an emergency measure after the failure of contraceptives.[4]

Abortion[5]

❖ Abortion is allowed for social, socio-economic, or socio-medical reasons up to 90 days.

❖ It is allowed for medical or eugenic reasons, or because of rape or other sexual crimes only, after 90 days.

❖ Women must have a doctor's certificate and wait at least one week.

❖ Minors need parental permission.

❖ Counseling is mandatory.

❖ Illegal abortions are numerous.

❖ Abortions are free of charge.

❖ Medical personnel who are opposed to abortion can, in advance, declare their conscientious objection, and may be excused from performing abortions.

Sex Education

❖ Sexuality education has been highly controversial and strongly influenced by the Catholic Church.[6]

❖ If it is provided, it is typically a lesson in a high school biology class.[6]

❖ The government removed all references to condoms in its campaign against AIDS.[7]

❖ Italy's Family Planning Association (UICEMP) focuses on information, education, and training courses for health service personnel and social workers in the state family planning clinics, for teachers, and for others working with young people.[8]

HIV/AIDS[9]

❖ An estimated 150,000 people were living with HIV/AIDS in Italy at the end of 2011.

❖ Early on in the epidemic the main route of transmission was through injecting drug users. However, in recent years, new infections are predominantly transmitted sexually; 30% of those infected are women.

LGBT issues[10]

❖ In 2013, anti-discrimination legislation was introduced to protect LGBT individuals.

❖ There is no recognition of same-sex couples.

❖ In Italy, only married couples can adopt, so gay and lesbian couples or single people are automatically excluded. The institution of custody can be granted to single people if a judge so rules.

❖ In Italy, gays were excluded in the military until 1985, when the ban was lifted.

Prostitution[11]

❖ Prostitution is legal.[11]

❖ Streetwalking is legal, but operating and working in a brothel are not.[11]

❖ Girls from Eastern Europe and West Africa have swelled street-walkers' numbers to an estimated 50,000. Around Milan, some 5,000 girls cater to about 60,000 customers a night.[12]

Pornography[13]

❖ Legal age for viewing pornography is 18 years.

Resources

▶ Associazione per la Ricerca in Sessuologia (ARS), Via Angelo Cappi 1/8. II 16126 Genova

▶ Centro Italiano di Sessuologia, Via della Lungarina, 65, Rome, 00153.

▶ Instituto di Sessuologia di Savona, 17026 Noli, Via la Malfa, 5, Savona

▶ Unione Italiana Educazione Matrimoniale e Prematrimoniale (UICEMP), Via Eugenio Chiesa 1, 20122 Milan Italy. Tel: 39 (02) 545 66 87.

JAMAICA

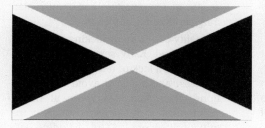

JAMAICA
POPULATION: **2,900,704**

CAPITAL: **KINGSTON**

Major Cities:	Kingston, Port Antonio, Montego Bay, Spanish Town
Ethnic Groups:	Black 91%, mixed 6%
Languages:	English, English patois
Major Religions:	Protestant 62%, Roman Catholic 3%
GDP per capita (PPP):	$9,300
Urban Population:	52%
Infant Mortality	14 per 1,000 births
Life Expectancy:	Females: 75 years; Males: 72 years
Literacy:	87%
Health Care System:	< 1 doctor per 1,000 people.

References
❏ *Reference World Atlas* (2013). NY: DK Publishing.
❏ *The World Almanac and Book of Facts 2013* (2012). NY: World Almanac Education Group.
❏ *The World Factbook https://www.cia.gov/library/publications/the-world-factbook/*

Sexual Activity

❖ The legal age of consent for heterosexuals and lesbians is 16. Male-to-male relations are illegal.[1]

❖ The mean age of first intercourse is 13.5 years old for boys and 15.8 years old for girls.[2]

❖ Jamaica has high levels of adolescent sexual activity and pregnancy. Forty percent of Jamaican women have been pregnant at least once before they reach the age of 20, and more than 80% of adolescent pregnancies are unplanned.[2]

Contraception

❖ Overall use of contraceptives includes 47% injections, 21% sterilization, 14% condoms, 10% pill, IUD 5% and 1% implant.[2]

❖ While condoms are the contraceptive of choice for teens, a study published in 2011 found that only half of teens who had sex in the past year had used a condom.[3]

❖ Emergency contraception is available without a prescription from a pharmacist. However, a study of pharmacists found that about half refused to dispense it. Many were uninformed or uncomfortable dispensing it.[4]

Abortion[5]

❖ The right to abortion is outlawed in Jamaica under the Offenses Against the Persons Act, which is modeled along the lines of an old English law of the same name, legislated in 1861. It prescribes life imprisonment for a woman who aborts her fetus and up to three years in jail for the doctor who helps her.

Sex Education

❖ Improving adolescent reproductive health and reducing teenage pregnancy rates are among Jamaica's top priorities resulting from the 1994 International Conference on Population and Development. The government plans to standardize and strengthen family life education programs and, among other activities, improve access to reproductive and family planning services for adolescents.[6]

❖ Sexuality education is lacking but there is a clear need. Early sexual activity, combined with a lack of relevant information, services, and skills to avoid risky situations, place Jamaican youth at risk of unintended pregnancies, sexually transmitted infections (STIs) including HIV, and other threats to their sexual and reproductive health.[7]

HIV/AIDS

❖ An estimated 30,000 people were living with HIV/AIDS in Jamaica in 2011.[8]

❖ High HIV infection rates have been found among sex workers (10%).[8]

❖ Nearly 30% of Jamaica's gay community is estimated to be infected with HIV.[9]

❖ In 2004, AIDS was the second leading cause of death for both young men and young women ages 15–24 in Jamaica. AIDS was also a leading cause of death among Jamaican children.[10]

LGBT issues

❖ Male-male sexual relationships are illegal in Jamaica and punishable up to 10 years in prison.[11]

❖ Jamaica is sometimes referred to by human rights groups as the most homophobic place on earth because of the high level of violence toward LGBT persons.[12]

Prostitution[13]

❖ Prostitution is illegal in Jamaica. However, it is widespread—especially in tourist areas. Human trafficking and child prostitutes are major issues.

Pornography

❖ IIn 2009, Jamaican regulators began forbidding all explicit references to sex and violence over the airwaves. The new rules from the island's broadcast commission ban any song or music video that depicts sexual acts or glorifies gun violence, murder, rape or arson.[14]

❖ Jamaica does not have a statutory law that prohibits pornography. It is a Common Law offence and a person may be prosecuted for it.[15]

Resource

▶ Jamaica Family Planning Association, *http://famplanjamaica.org/*

▶ Jamaica National Family Planning Board *http://www.jnfpb.org/*

JAPAN

JAPAN

POPULATION: 127,253,075

CAPITAL: **TOKYO**

Major Cities:	Tokyo, Osaka, Nagoya, Sapporo, Kyoto
Ethnic Groups:	Japanese 99%
Languages:	Japanese (official)
Major Religions:	Buddhism and Shintoism shared by 84%
GDP per capita (PPP):	$32,900
Urban Population:	91%
Infant Mortality:	2 per 1,000 births
Life Expectancy:	Females: 88 years; Males: 81 years
Literacy:	99%
Health Care System:	The combination of public & private funding has created an insurance pension system for hospitals, clinics, physicians; 2 doctors per 1,000 people.

References

❏ *Reference World Atlas* (2013). NY: DK Publishing.
❏ *The World Almanac and Book of Facts 2013* (2012). NY: World Almanac Education Group.
❏ *The World Factbook https://www.cia.gov/library/publications/the-world-factbook/*

Sexual Activity

❖ The legal age of consent is 13. However, prefecture law usually overrides federal law, raising the age up to 18.[1]

❖ Official figures show that Japanese schoolchildren are having more sex than ever before, and that many are shunning condoms, unaware of the risks of contracting HIV and other sexually transmitted infections (STIs). A 2005 survey found nearly 40 per cent of senior high school students aged 15 to 18 have had sex. Nearly half of 17-year-old girls have had sex, compared with 17 per cent in 1990.[2]

Contraception

❖ Birth control pills were not legalized in Japan until 1996.[3]

❖ The choice of modern contraceptive methods is very limited. Low-dose pills, IUDs, injectables, and implants have not been approved for use and the diaphragm is no longer produced in Japan due to lack of demand.[4]

❖ High dose oral contraceptives are prescribed to between 500,000 and 800,000 women for supposedly therapeutic purposes such as menstrual disorders, but in reality they are used for contraception. As a consequence, Japanese women tend to have a negative view of the Pill.[4]

❖ As contraceptive choices are so limited in Japan, more than 80% of couples use the condom.[4]

Abortion[5]

❖ Legal restrictions were lifted in 1948, legalizing abortion in the first 5 months of pregnancy (decades before other industrialized countries). All legal abortions must be performed within medical facilities at the compliance of a physician assigned by a local medical association. When the pregnancy is a result of rape or incest, the abortion can be performed without the legal consent of the woman.

❖ Married women seeking an abortion must have the consent of her spouse.

❖ Japan has an average of 250,000 abortions per year.

❖ The abortion rate has declined by 47% since 1975—many point to the availability of the pill.

Sex Education

❖ Sex education in schools is poor, and teenagers are often left without sufficient family planning information and services.[4]

❖ Guidelines for HIV/AIDS education in schools set by the Ministry of Education:[6]

1) As a part of hygiene education, all grade schools must teach students that HIV is a blood-borne infection.

2) Middle schools will teach students about HIV/AIDS in the context of other sexually transmitted diseases.

3) High schools are permitted to mention condoms as protection against HIV infection.

❖ The Ministry of Education believes that teachers should teach HIV/AIDS prevention to students without mentioning sexual intercourse.[6]

HIV/AIDS[7]

❖ An estimated 7,900 people were living with HIV/AIDS in Japan at the end of 2011.

❖ Most reported HIV/AIDS cases in Japan during the mid-to-late 1980s and early 1990s were due to HIV infected blood products that were imported for the treatment of hemophilia patients; a third of the AIDS cases (33.3%) reported in 1988 were in hemophilia patients infected through imported blood coagulation factor products. The high percentage of hemophilia AIDS cases is still the distinctive characteristic of HIV infection in Japan and is not seen in other countries in the world.

- Today most newly diagnosed HIV infections appear to have been acquired through sexual contact between men having sex with men.

LGBT issues[8]

- There are no laws against same-sex relations in Japan, nor any legal recognition.
- In 1995, following international pressure from gay groups, the Japanese Society of Psychiatry and Neurology removed homosexuality from its list of disorders. The society will now rely on the World Health Organization's disease-classification manual, which does not consider being gay an illness.
- In 2003, the government agency that rents apartments to couples began renting to same-sex couples.
- In 2008, a law was passed allowing transgender individuals to change their legal gender status after surgery.
- In 2009, Japan began allowing its citizens to marry their same-sex partner overseas in countries where it is legal.

Prostitution[9]

- Vaginal prostitution is against the law, while fellatio prostitution is legal, as women who perform fellatio for money are not considered prostitutes in Japan.

Pornography

- The Japanese government has proposed to set up an independent search to control the transmission of obscene or criminal material over the Internet.[10]
- Sexually explicit comics for women are quite popular and they often seem to feature rape themes or other depictions of forced sexual submission.[11]
- Nearly 80% of commercial child pornography on the Internet originates in Japan. Possession of child pornography is legal; however, the production, sale and distribution is illegal.[12]

Resources

- Family Planning Federation of Japan, Hoken Kaikan Shinkan Bldg, 1-10 Ichigaya Tamachi, Shinjuku, Tokyo 162-0843.
- Japanese Association for Sex Education. (JASE). Miyata Bldg. 1-3 Kanada Jinbocho, Chiyoda-Ku, Tokyo 101.

- Japanese Association of Sex Educators, Counselors and Therapists (JASECT), JASE Clinic, 3F Shin-Anoyama Bldg. (West), 1-1 Minami, Aoyama, 1-chome Minato-Ku, Tokyo 107.
- Japan Institute for Research in Education. 4-3-6-702 Kozimachi Chiyodaku, Tokyo 7102

KENYA

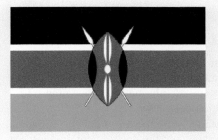

KENYA

POPULATION: 44,037,656

CAPITAL: **NAIROBI**

Major Cities:	Nairobi, Mombasa
Ethnic Groups:	Kikuyu 22%, Luhya 14%, Luo 13%, Kalenjin 12%, Kamba 11%
Languages:	Kiswahili, English (both official), numerous indigenous languages
Major Religions:	Protestant 47%, Roman Catholic 23%, Muslim 11%
GDP per capita (PPP):	$1,800
Urban Population:	24%
Infant Mortality:	42 per 1,000 live births
Life Expectancy:	Females: 65 years; Males: 62 years
Adult Literacy:	87%
Health Care System:	< 1 doctor per 1,000 people

References

❏ *Reference World Atlas* (2013). NY: DK Publishing.
❏ *The World Almanac and Book of Facts 2013* (2012). NY: World Almanac Education Group.
❏ *The World Factbook https://www.cia.gov/library/publications/the-world-factbook/*

Sexual Activity

❖ The legal age of consent is 18 for hetero-sexuals and lesbians; it is illegal for homosexuals.[1]

❖ Most women have their first child before age 18.[2]

❖ First sexual contact can be as early as 10–12 in both boys and girls; sexuality has a lot to do with culture, education, family units and economic factors.[2]

❖ Young girls who become pregnant are expelled from school.[2]

Contraception

❖ There is general knowledge about con-traception among youths, but little prac-tical information and much misinforma-tion about side effects hinder the use of modern contraceptives.[2]

❖ Culture and religious beliefs prohibit the use of contraception.[3]

❖ Government is reluctant to teach adoles-cents about contraception, or provide it to unmarried women.[3]

❖ An estimated 39% of married women report using contraception; with about a third using modern methods.[4]

❖ Only 12% of Kenyan men currently use condoms.[4]

Abortion[5]

❖ Abortion is illegal unless the girl or woman's life is at risk.

❖ Abortion is not an uncommon experi-ence, especially among young, single, urban women.

❖ In Kenya unsafe abortions are wide-spread and threaten women's health. Reports maintain that one-third of maternal deaths are due to illegal, unsafe abortions. Severe complications of illegal abortion are most common in girls ages 10–19 (45%).

❖ From the evidence in the 2013 report on Kenya's unsafe abortions is clear that improving women's access to affordable and effective family planning and/or contraception is key to preventing unin-tended pregnancy and unsafe abortion.

Sex Education

❖ In the absence of traditional sources of information, young people turn to their peers for information concerning issues relating to sex.[2]

❖ Many schools are run by religious orders, and the government opposes sex education in the school.[3]

HIV/AIDS[6]

❖ An estimated 1.6 million people were living with HIV/AIDS in Kenya at the end of 2011. HIV represents the greatest health challenge for Kenya.

❖ As is the case in many African countries, HIV prevalence in Kenya is higher among women than among men (58%). Therefore, the focus has been on pre-venting transmission to newborns; 69% of pregnant women received drugs to prevent transmission in 2011.

❖ The number of new AIDS cases in 2011 was one-third of number reported 20 years ago.

❖ Thirty percent of sex workers are HIV positive.

❖ Kenya is in the forefront of a voluntary male circumcision for HIV prevention.

❖ Kenya requires HIV testing for couples wishing to get married.

❖ There has been a 10% reduction in world assistance due to global financial difficulties.

❖ Knowledge of one's status though test-ing has been a major strategy in the AIDS epidemic.

❖ 15 million condoms are distributed monthly.

LGBT issues[7]

❖ A 2007 study found 96% of Kenyans are opposed to same-sex relations.[7]

❖ Sections 162 to 165 of the Penal Code criminalize same sex behavior and attempted same-sex behavior between men, referring to it as "carnal knowledge against the order of nature." The penalty is 5 to 14 years' imprisonment. Lesbian relations are not mentioned in the law.[8]

❖ Kenyan law defines any sexual relations between men as a criminal act. There are, however, few prosecutions; one exception is a 1998 investigation into the Forum for Positive Generation on AIDS Prevention, a registered community organization for people with HIV in Kisumu. Police alleged that the organization has been "recruiting" people to be gay.[8]

Prostitution

❖ Prostitution is illegal, but widespread.[9]

❖ Young men frequent prostitutes, often for their first sexual encounter.[2]

❖ In an economy with too few jobs, single women without education are turning to prostitution.[9]

❖ A great number of women in the cities who have been abandoned by men or in need of extra income also turn to prostitution.[9]

❖ Many sex workers are married.[9]

Pornography

❖ All forms of erotica and sexually oriented publications are illegal in Kenya, and not available for sale. This includes publications featuring nudity, which is culturally offensive.[10]

Resources

▶ Family Planning Association of Kenya
   http://www.fhok.org/

▶ International Planned Parenthood Federation-Africa Region, Box 30234, Nairobi, Kenya. Tel: 254-2/720280

MEXICO

**MEXICO
(UNITED MEXICAN STATES)**
POPULATION: 116,220,947

CAPITAL: **MEXICO CITY**

Major Cities:	Mexico City, Guadalajara, Puebla
Ethnic Groups:	Mestizo 60%, Amerindian 30%, White 9%
Languages:	Spanish (official) and Mayan dialects
Major Religions:	Roman Catholic 83%, Protestant 2%
GDP per capita (PPP):	$15,600
Urban Population:	77%
Infant Mortality:	16 per 1,000 live births
Life Expectancy:	Females: 80 years; Males: 74 years
Adult Literacy:	91%
Health Care System:	Social welfare; 3 doctors per 1,000 people.

References
❏ *Reference World Atlas* (2013). NY: DK Publishing.
❏ *The World Almanac and Book of Facts 2013* (2012). NY: World Almanac Education Group.
❏ *The World Factbook https://www.cia.gov/library/publications/the-world-factbook/*

Sexual Activity

❖ The legal age of consent is 12 for hetero-sexuals, and 18 for homosexuals.[1]

❖ The average age of women at first birth is 21.[2]

Contraception

❖ In Mexico, where the government pro-vides contraceptive services and meth-ods free of charge, public-sector family planning services meet the contraceptive needs of 72 % of the population.[3]

❖ Mexican law provides that maternal and infant health care and family planning are to be considered basic health serv-ices, and the former is considered a pri-ority. The family planning laws and poli-cies are outlined in the Mexican Regulation on Family Planning Services and in the Reproductive Health and Family Planning Program.[4]

❖ The family planning services provided by the government include information, orientation, counseling, selection, pre-scription, and distribution of contracep-tive methods. These services and the contraceptive methods are free of charge. In particular, public services pro-vide oral hormonal methods, injectable methods, IUDs, sterilization, vasectomy, barrier methods, and spermicides.[4]

❖ Emergency contraception is available over-the-counter.[4]

❖ The General Health Law establishes that family planning services are a priority within the general provision of health services. The objectives of the family planning subprogram are: to strengthen and broaden the coverage and quality of family planning information, education and services, with special emphasis on rural areas; to contribute to a decrease in fertility; to reduce the number of unwanted, unplanned and high-risk pregnancies; and to broaden activities designed to diversify the use of modern contraceptive methods. [4]

❖ In Mexico, surgical sterilization is the most common family planning method and has a prevalence rate of 43 % among women of childbearing age. However, research has revealed that one-fourth of sterilized women claimed not to have been informed of the irreversible nature of the operation, or of alternative contra-ceptive methods available at the time; 39 % claimed not to have signed the con-sent form.[4]

Abortion

❖ The Decree of 2 January 1931, as amended 16 February 1971, made abor-tion illegal except in cases of medical or legal grounds to save the life of the woman or in cases of rape or incest. Some interpretations allow abortion in order to preserve the physical health of the woman, although this interpretation varies from state to state.[4]

❖ Most abortions are performed during the first trimester. They must be performed by a physician with the corroboration of another physician as to the necessity of the procedure. The consent of the woman and her husband (or in the case of teens, a parent or guardian) is required.[4]

❖ The abortion laws in Mexico are less harsh than in other Latin American countries, but abortion continues to be illegal in most cases. Women of means can have safe abortions, while poor women have to resort to abortions in extremely unsafe conditions.[4]

❖ In 2007, Mexico City legalized abortion during the first 12 weeks. As a result several states tightened their abortion restrictions by amending state constitu-tions to recognize the "right to life: beginning at conception."[5]

❖ Despite the harsh restrictions, the esti-mated total number of abortions in Mexico is 875,000 per year. Their rate is 40 % higher than the U.S. where abor-tion is legal.[5]

- Abortion is the third or fourth greatest cause of death in Mexico.[5]
- Abortion ranges from the second to the fourth greatest reason for hospitalization in Mexico; 17% of women sought medical treatment for complications from abortion.[5]

Sex Education

- In general, Mexican adolescents receive information about contraception too late, and they tend to receive sex education that emphasizes biological facts over decision-making skills.[6]
- The majority of young people in Mexico confront the risks of sexual relations with little information and a great deal of mystification. They receive little or no advice as to how to deal with their sexuality in a responsible way; they have poor knowledge about reproductive health; and they have only limited access to contraceptive services and methods. However, despite the obvious need for urgent action, programs to improve young people's sexual and reproductive health are the subject of controversy long before they are introduced. A small number of conservative groups that have significant influence in Mexico are always present in the debate, censoring everything from the content of chapters on sexual education in government textbooks to messages about safe sex in the press. These groups advocate sexual abstinence, no sex outside of marriage and the withholding of information about contraception from young people so as to "alienate" them from sex.[4]

HIV/AIDS[7]

- An estimated 180,000 people were living with HIV/AIDS in Mexico at the end of 2011—as many as two thirds of them were men who are believed to have been infected during sex with other men.

- There are signs that heterosexual transmission of HIV is increasing as more women are infected by their partners who also have sex with men.
- Stigma and discrimination are a problem in prevention, testing, and treatment.

LGBT issues[8]

- In 2010, same-sex couples made history in Mexico City by marrying under the first law in Latin America that explicitly approves gay marriage. The legislation allows only residents of Mexico's capital to marry, although marriages will be recognized in other states.
- The Mexican Constitution states that men and women are equal. Education should promote the ideals of "fraternity and equal rights of all mankind, avoiding privileges of race, sects, groups, sexes or individuals." This law is not effectively enforced. Amnesty International cites Mexico's homosexual men and women to be the most likely victims of abuse and violence.
- Beginning Oct. 1, 1999, Penal Code Article 281 prohibited discrimination "based on age, sex, pregnancy, marital status, race, language, religion, ideology, sexual orientation, skin color, nationality, social origin or position, work or profession, economic status, physical features or health." The penalty for violation of the law is one to three years in prison and/or a fine equal to 50 to 200 days' salary and/or 25 to 100 days of community service. The law prohibits provocation or incitement of hate or violence, and bans bias in employment and public accommodations and services.

Prostitution[9]

- Larger cities have "zona roja" where prostitution is allowed. Prostitutes are registered, get health checks and must carry a card to prove it.

❖ Cab drivers know the locations of prostitutes and will drive customers to those locations and wait for them.

Pornography[10]

❖ The hardest pornography openly available is equivalent to *Hustler* or *Penthouse*.[10]

❖ Video stores carry pornographic movies, but don't display the boxes.[10]

❖ It is illegal to sell or show a child under 18 years of age pornography. However recent reports have found that Mexico is the #2 producer of child porn, using children trafficked from India.[11]

Resources

▶ Fundacion Mexican Para la Planeacion Familiar (MEXFAM)
http://www.mexfam.org.mx/

▶ National AIDS Committee, Secretary for Health, Lieja Numero 7, Col. Juarez, 1er Piso, 04360 Mexico City, DF, Mexico. Tel: (5) 554-9112

▶ International Gay and Lesbian Association-Mexico (Associacion Lesbia y Gay Internacional-Mexico), Apartado Postal 1-1693, 06030 Mexico City, DF, Mexico

MOROCCO

MOROCCO
POPULATION: 32,649,130
CAPITAL: **RATAT**

Major Cities:	Rabat, Agadir, Safi, Meknes
Ethnic Groups:	Arab-Berber 99%
Languages:	Arabic (official), Berber dialects, French often the language of business, government, and diplomacy
Major Religions:	Muslim 99%
GDP per capita (PPP):	$5,400
Urban Population:	57%
Infant Mortality:	26 per 1,000 births
Life Expectancy:	Females: 80 years; Males: 73 years
Adult Literacy:	56%
Health Care System:	< 1 doctor per 1,000 people

References

❑ *Reference World Atlas* (2013). NY: DK Publishing.
❑ *The World Almanac and Book of Facts 2013* (2012). NY: World Almanac Education Group.
❑ *The World Factbook https://www.cia.gov/library/publications/the-world-factbook/*

Sexual Activity[1]

❖ The legal age of consent is 15 for hetero-sexuals (this is also the legal age of marriage). Same-sex activity is illegal.[1]

❖ Morocco is a Muslim culture, in which Islamic law condemns prostitution, same-sex relations, and sex outside of marriage.[2]

❖ Marriage is the only setting in which sexual activity is allowed under Islam and in which pregnancy and childbearing are legally legitimate.[2]

❖ Girls grow up aspiring to marriage and motherhood. They are instilled with the belief that their bodies are the source of somewhat mysterious problems, and they are ordered to remain "pure" (virgins) until they marry.[2]

Contraception[3]

❖ Data on contraceptive use by sexually active, unmarried adolescents are unavailable, since premarital sex is not acceptable or acknowledged.

❖ Approximately 40% of married women use contraceptive methods; the most common methods include the Pill (71%), IUD (8%) and sterilization (7%).

Abortion

❖ Abortion is limited to saving the life of the mother. The intervention must be "openly performed" within six weeks of pregnancy by a physician with the consent of the spouse.[3]

❖ Because of the disgrace that unwed pregnancy represents, and the social, economic and legal difficulties that unwed mothers have to face, illegal abortion is quite common.[2]

❖ Estimates indicate that 130,000 to 150,000 illegal abortions are performed each year.[2]

Sex Education[2]

❖ Sex education is taboo.

❖ While some religious scholars in Morocco oppose sexuality education and condom promotion for unmarried youth as a transgression of the Koran, others stress that the hadith includes clear guidelines for sexuality education.

HIV/AIDS

❖ An estimated 32,000 people were living with HIV/AIDS at the end of 2011.[4]

❖ Due to the lack of sex education, STIs are believed to be transmitted in the direction of woman to man. This attitude appears to exempt men of the responsibility to prevent STIs.[2]

LGBT issues[5]

❖ Male homosexuality is illegal and considered a punishable offense. It carries a penalty of between 6 months and 3 years imprisonment and additional fines for "lewd or unnatural acts with an individual of the same sex."

❖ Female homosexuality is not mentioned in the Koran. It is thought to be prevalent in certain regions of Morocco, particularly the north, but remains hidden, unmentioned, and unstudied.

Prostitution[6]

❖ Morocco is becoming an important location for those seeking sex workers. Prostitution is both heterosexual and homosexual and sex workers are young.

❖ Unemployment, poverty, migration, urbanization, the tourism industry, and the common practice among boys and young men of seeking the services of a sex worker, particularly to initiate their sexual lives, lead to high levels of formal and informal prostitution.

Pornography

❖ The possession of pornography (e.g., documents, films, magazines) is banned and constitutes a criminal offense.

Resource

▶ Association Marocaine De Planification Familiale (AMPF) *www.ampf.org.ma*

NEPAL

NEPAL

POPULATION: 30,430,267

CAPITAL: **KATHMANDU**

Major Cities:	Kathmandu, Patan, Bhaktapur, Nepalgunj, Birgunj
Ethnic Groups:	Chhettri 15%, Brahman-Hill 13%, Magar 7%, Tharu 7%, Tamang 6%, Newar 5%, Muslim 4%
Languages:	Nepali 48%, Maithali 12%, Bhojpuri 7%
Major Religions:	Hindu 81%, Buddhist 11%, Muslim 4%, Kirant 4%
GDP per capita (PPP):	$5,400
Urban Population:	17%
Infant Mortality:	42 per 1,000 births
Life Expectancy:	Females: 68 years; Males: 66 years
Adult Literacy:	60%
Health Care System:	< 1 doctor per 1,000 people

References
❑ *Reference World Atlas* (2013). NY: DK Publishing.
❑ *The World Almanac and Book of Facts 2013* (2012). NY: World Almanac Education Group.
❑ *The World Factbook https://www.cia.gov/library/publications/the-world-factbook/*

Sexual Activity[1]

❖ The legal age of consent is 16, but there are still child marriages taking place in rural parts of Nepal for children under 16.

Contraception[2]

❖ The most commonly used methods of contraceptives are the Pill, IUD and injectables (all used by women).

❖ Condoms are available in hospitals, health care centers, and health posts.

❖ The taboo associated with pre-marital sex still affects men and women from getting contraceptives without getting embarrassed or ashamed.

Abortion[3]

❖ Abortions in Nepal were illegal until 2002, when the government changed the law to allow qualified and author-ized health workers to terminate preg-nancies.

❖ Nepal began training health-care providers in comprehensive abortion care in 2004. As a result, approxi-mately 160,000 women have been served in public and private facilities; nearly 500 providers, including nurses, have been trained; and 74 out of 75 districts have at least one trained provider. But despite these successes, many poor, rural women still cannot access safe abortion services.

❖ Illegal abortions are still a leading cause of maternal death; Nepal has one of the highest maternal death rates in the world.

Sex Education[4]

❖ Although Nepal's secondary school education curriculum includes sex education in classes 9 and 10, within which HIV/AIDS is taught, these classes tend to be highly biomedical in focus and the time allocated to the subject remains limited, if it is covered at all. Furthermore, teachers have no opportunity for the training, and lack of skills as well as instructional resources to deliver a comprehensive HIV/AIDS education.

HIV/AIDS[5]

❖ An estimated 49,000 people were living with HIV/AIDS at the end of 2011.

❖ People who inject drugs, men who have sex with men and female sex workers are the key populations at risk. In addition, migrant workers who travel to high HIV prevalent areas in India where they visit sex workers are also playing a role.

LGBT issues[6]

❖ The Blue Diamond Society was estab-lished in 2001; it works for sexual minorities in a country where Hindu conservative religion and society based on Hinduism condemns sexual behavior other than heterosexual rela-tions. They estimate there are 500,000 people, including men who have sex with men and transgender persons.[6]

❖ The decision of Nepal's Supreme Court in 2007 ordered the government to grant rights to sexual and gender minorities.[6]

❖ In 2007, Nepal added a third gender category to census surveys, opening the doors to recognition of sexual and gender minorities who may not fit the "male" "female" category.[7]

Prostitution[8]

❖ Prostitution is illegal in Nepal.

❖ Every year around 10,000 Nepalese girls, most between the age of 9 and 16, are sold to brothels in India. More than 200,000 Nepalese girls are involved in the Indian sex trade.

❖ Nepalese women who are trafficked and prostituted in debt bondage in India's sex industry are forced to work longer hours and have more clients than local women.

Pornography[9]

❖ As DVD cameras, mobile phones, computers and the Internet become affordable and accessible, more and more Nepalis are using the technology for filming and distributing pornography. Combined with tourism, the trend has made Nepal one of the points of origin for pornographic films and even pedophilic material on the Web.

Resource

▶ Family Planning Association of Nepal (FPAN) *www.fpan.org*

NETHERLANDS

NETHERLANDS

POPULATION: 16,805,037

CAPITAL: **AMSTERDAM**

Major Cities:	Amsterdam, Rotterdam, The Hague
Ethnic Groups:	Dutch 81%
Languages:	Dutch (official), Frisian (official)
Major Religions:	Roman Catholic 30%, Dutch reformed 11%, Calvinist 6%, Muslim 6%
GDP per capita (PPP):	$42,900
Urban Population:	83%
Infant mortality:	4 per 1,000 births
Life Expectancy:	Females: 83 years; Males: 79 years
Adult Literacy:	99%
Health Care System:	Hospitals and private physicians; 1 doctor per 400 people.

References

❑ *Reference World Atlas* (2013). NY: DK Publishing.
❑ *The World Almanac and Book of Facts 2013* (2012). NY: World Almanac Education Group.
❑ *The World Factbook https://www.cia.gov/library/publications/the-world-factbook/*

Sexual Activity

❖ The legal age of consent for sex is 16. However, Dutch law permits a young person between 12 and 16 to have sexual relationships as long as the young person consents.[1]

❖ Most Dutch teens begin their sexual career with "French" kissing and hugging at around age 14.[2]

❖ The Netherlands has one of the lowest teen pregnancy rates in the world.

❖ Most of 18–19 year olds have experienced sexual intercourse.[2]

Contraception

❖ Young people in the Netherlands have a high level of effective contraceptive use. Nearly 85% use contraception at first intercourse. Pill use is extremely high. "Double Dutch"—the use of the Pill and condom together for protection from pregnancy and diseases—is used by many of those who are sexually active.[2]

❖ Oral contraception, as well as other 'medical' methods of contraception have been available free of charge in The Netherlands since 1972. Condoms are not funded.[3]

❖ Emergency contraception, commonly known as "the morning after pill," has been available since the 1960's.[4]

Abortion

❖ The Netherlands has one of the lowest abortion rates in Europe.[5]

❖ Abortion is available for free on demand if the woman is 16 or older and is in a situation of emergency.[6]

❖ Consultation with a doctor followed by a five-day waiting period is necessary before an abortion is performed.[6]

❖ Abortion is permitted up to 22 weeks; almost all abortions are performed before the 8th week of pregnancy.[6]

❖ RU-486 (Mifepristone) was approved for marketing in 1999.[7]

Sex Education[8]

❖ Sexuality education typically begins at home with parents.

❖ Sex education in schools is not compulsory. However, since 1993 some compulsory core objectives, for both primary and secondary education, have been put into place.

❖ Sexuality education is focused on encouraging young people to gain autonomy in their own attitudes and behavior regarding sexuality. It gives young people not only the medical and health knowledge, but also the skills to negotiate relationships and understand emotional as well as physical side of sexuality.

❖ Sex education is also available through youth clubs, evening classes for adults, and is also covered by the mass media.

HIV/AIDS

❖ An estimated 25,000 people were living with HIV/AIDS at the end of 2011.[9]

❖ HIV testing is systematic for blood donors and for some insurance applicants.[9]

❖ From 2004 universal screening in pregnant women in the Netherlands started.[9]

❖ From January 1st 2002, a registration is coordinated by the HIV Monitoring Foundation in Amsterdam and is based on the 22 HIV/AIDS treatment centers in the Netherlands.[9]

❖ The "Double Dutch" campaign gave a double message: use a condom to prevent disease and the Pill to prevent pregnancy. This approach was promoted when AIDS first became a major issue in the late 1980s.[2]

LGBT issues

❖ The Dutch Penal Code bans discrimination on the basis of "hetero- or homosexual orientation." Article One of the Constitution also prohibits discrimination based on sexual orientation. The Equal Treatment Commission provides redress from discrimination in work-, education- and service-related situations.[10]

❖ On April 1, 2001, The Netherlands became the first country in the world to offer same-sex couples the freedom to marry, providing gay and lesbian people the full range of protections, responsibilities, and benefits that come with civil marriage, including adoption.[11]

❖ There are no remaining anti-lesbian or anti-gay provisions in Dutch Criminal Law. Until 1971, lesbian and gay sex between an adult and a minor (meaning under 21) was an offence. Today, the Worldwide Ages of Consent is 16 years for lesbians, gays and straights.[12]

❖ In 1974, there was an abolition of the ban on gays in the military.[13]

Prostitution[14]

❖ Prostitution is legal, and in 2000, brothels also became legal for the first time since 1912. The intention of the new law is to turn "sex work" into just another job, complete with employment rights and even a trade union. There is no evidence that prostitution has increased as a result: indeed the famous red-light district in Amsterdam is, if anything, smaller than it once was.

❖ Most prostitutes seem to dislike their new legal status, because it has forced them to pay taxes, and it has made it easier for the police to drive illegal immigrants out of the business. But they also admit that the Netherlands has done more than most to separate organized crime from sex work.

❖ Prostitutes must be at least 18; clients must be at least 16. Violation of either age limit is a crime for the other party.

❖ Window prostitution is the most visible form, though it only takes up about 20% of the entire sex industry in the Netherlands.

Pornography[15]

❖ The Netherlands has very liberal laws. Pornography is sold openly at normal newsstands.

❖ Material involving animals were declared illegal in 2006 due to new animal-welfare laws.

Resources

▶ Rutgers World Population Fund, *http://www.rutgerswpf.nl/*

▶ The Netherlands Institute for Health Promotion and Disease Prevention (NIGZ), *http://www.nigz.nl*

NEW ZEALAND

NEW ZEALAND

POPULATION: 4,365,113

CAPITAL: **WELLINGTON**

Major Cities:	Auckland, Wellington, Christchurch
Ethnic Groups:	New Zealand European 57%, Asian 8%, Maori 7%, Pacific islander 5%
Languages:	English (official) 92%, Maori (official) 4%
Major Religions:	Protestant 39%, Roman Catholic 15%
GDP per capita (PPP):	$30,200
Urban Population:	86%
Infant Mortality:	5 per 1,000 births
Life Expectancy:	Females: 83 years; Males: 79 years
Adult Literacy:	99%
Health Care System:	70% publicly funded, with private physicians and clinics bridging the gap in waiting for services; midwifery subsidized; 2 doctors per 1,000 people.

References
❏ *Reference World Atlas* (2013). NY: DK Publishing.
❏ *The World Almanac and Book of Facts 2013* (2012). NY: World Almanac Education Group.
❏ *The World Factbook https://www.cia.gov/library/publications/the-world-factbook/*

Sexual Activity

- The legal age for sexual consent is 16 years old.[1]
- The rising rate of teen pregnancy is a growing public issue.[2]

Contraception

- Age of consent for medical treatment is as low as 14 in parts of New Zealand.[3]
- In an effort to lower New Zealand's abortion rate, the government offers free birth control pills to women.[4]
- The Pill and female sterilization are the most popular methods.[5]
- Emergency contraception is available over-the-counter in New Zealand.[6]

Abortion

- Abortion is available to women in their first trimester, from regular physicians in licensed institutions. The procedure is free if performed at a public hospital. After the first trimester, abortions are available within an institution with "full license," and with the approval of a committee of three: two certifying physicians, one of which is an OB/GYN, and the operating surgeon. Counseling of the mother is a prerequisite.[2]
- Abortions can be obtained in order to save the woman's life, to preserve the physical or mental health of the mother, in cases of rape or incest, fetal impairment or for economic or social reasons.[2]
- RU-486 (Mifepristone) is available for early abortion in New Zealand.[7]

Sex Education

- The FPA of New Zealand launched 'The Word—on sex, life and relationships,' a multi-media awareness campaign to provide young people aged 12–15, with information about relationships, sexuality and sexual health. 'The Word' involved radio advertising, a free telephone information line and a free booklet. Twelve thousand calls were received within the first week. Young people say that 'The Word' is straight to the point, easy to read, and that they particularly like the dictionary contained in the booklet.[8]
- A major study in New Zealand showed that teaching safer sex using tactics of fear, monogamy or abstinence increased the incidence of unsafe sex in high-risk individuals and so increased the spread of HIV. The study also found that anti-discrimination legislation, and teaching of tolerance of homosexuality, helped decrease the spread of AIDS.[9]

HIV/AIDS

- An estimated 2,600 people were living with HIV/AIDS in New Zealand at the end of 2011. Much of the cases are attributable to HIV diagnoses among men who have sex with men.[10]
- One in three new HIV infections are the result of heterosexual contact.[10]
- Early in the epidemic (1987), New Zealand began offering needle exchange programs to avert HIV transmission through IV drug use.[10]
- In 1993, a law was passed which banned discrimination because of the presence of disease, including HIV and Hepatitis.[11]

LGBT issues

- The New Zealand Human Rights Act includes protection based on sexual orientation in employment, education, access to public places, provision of goods and services, and housing and accommodation.[12]
- Homosexual Law Reform Act became law in 1986. It was an Act to amend the Crimes Act 1961 by removing criminal sanctions against consensual same-sex conduct between males, and by consequentially amending the law relating to consensual anal intercourse. In effect, consenting adult gay (male) sexual behavior was decriminalized and the

age of adult consent was changed to sixteen years, equating to the age of consent for heterosexual sexual behavior.[13]

❖ The New Zealand Bill of Rights Act of 1990 provides that everyone has the right to freedom from discrimination on grounds which include sex, marital status, family status, and sexual orientation.[13]

❖ In 2005, New Zealand's parliament passed legislation to recognize civil unions between gay couples. In 2013 they legalized same-sex marriage.[13]

Prostitution[14]

❖ Prostitution is legal.

❖ In June 2003, a bill was passed in Parliament that legalized prostitution, pimping and brothel-keeping. Brothel keepers must apply for an operator's license although this is formality unless the person has a serious criminal conviction.

Pornography[15]

❖ The Films, Videos and Publications Act of 1993 covers publications of all types (audio/visual, written, or computerized). The legislation calls for levels of classification: unrestricted is labeled green and is available to anyone; unrestricted with a yellow label is available only to certain ages; restricted is given a red label and is available to certain ages; objectionable "describes, depicts or otherwise deals with matters such as sex, horror, crime, cruelty or violence . . . to be injurious to the public good."

Resource

▶ New Zealand Family Planning Association (NZPFA) *http://www.familyplanning.org.nz/*

NORWAY

Major Cities:	Oslo, Bergen, Trondheim, Stavanger
Ethnic Groups:	Norwegian 94%, Sami
Languages:	Norwegian (official)
Major Religions:	Church of Norway 86%
GDP per capita (PPP):	$55,900
Urban Population:	79%
Infant Mortality:	3 per 1,000 births
Life Expectancy:	Females: 83 years; Males: 78 years
Adult Literacy:	100%
Health Care System:	4 doctors per 1,000 people.

References

❏ *Reference World Atlas* (2013). NY: DK Publishing.

❏ *The World Almanac and Book of Facts 2013* (2012). NY: World Almanac Education Group.

❏ *The World Factbook https://www.cia.gov/library/publications/the-world-factbook/*

Sexual Activity

❖ The legal age of consent is 16 years old.[1]
❖ Nearly 60% of young women surveyed said they began having sex before age 18.[2]

Contraception

❖ All contraceptives are widely available, and contraceptive use is high.[3]
❖ Use of IUDs or implants is higher than many other countries: 25% of women use these.[4]
❖ A study in 2010 targeting several areas with high abortion rates found that the teen abortion rate was cut in half when contraceptives were made available free of charge.[5]
❖ Emergency contraception is easily available over-the-counter.[6]

Abortion[7]

❖ In January of 1979, a law was passed to make abortion legal up to twelve weeks gestation.
❖ After twelve weeks, a board of doctors makes the decision whether or not to abort the fetus.
❖ Girls under 16 must obtain parental consent.
❖ RU-486 (Mifepristone) was approved for marketing in 2000.

Sex Education[8]

❖ Norway has a liberal climate and a positive approach to sexuality education.
❖ Sexuality education has been available in schools since the 1950s and has been mandatory since the 1970s.
❖ The Norwegian Association for Sexuality and Reproductive Health, produce a regular newsletter. They also conduct research on adolescent sexual, contraceptive and abortion behavior, as well as providing sex education seminars.

HIV/AIDS[9]

❖ An estimated 4,500 people were living with HIV/AIDS in Norway at the end of 2011.
❖ HIV testing is systematic for blood donors, pregnant women (including women having abortions) and STI patients.
❖ Diagnosed HIV cases are reported in a national HIV database using an identifying code.
❖ Treatment is covered 100%.

LGBT issues

❖ LGBT persons are accepted in Norway. Laws prohibiting discrimination on the grounds of sexual orientation were introduced in 1981.[10]
❖ In 2009 same-sex marriage was legalized.[11]

Prostitution[12]

❖ Prostitution was legal in Norway until 2009 when the law changed in an attempt to deal with human trafficking. The new law follows Sweden: the client will be arrested (not the prostitute).
❖ As part of the change, prostitutes will be offered access to free education and health care/drug treatment.
❖ Pimping and procuring were already illegal.

Pornography

❖ Hardcore material is illegal to produce, distribute and sell, but legal to possess. One may acquire it abroad, on the Internet, or via satellite TV. There are also some illegal porn shops, especially in the larger cities. To satisfy legal requirements, editors of erotic magazines, domestic TV channels and cable TV have obscured *sexual organs in activity* using black rectangles etc. After the Supreme Court in December 2005 unanimously acquitted a former magazine editor for publishing unobscured hardcore pornography in 2002, however, it is understood that printed hardcore pornography is no longer illegal, and it is expected that pornographic magazines will be introduced in general stores.[13]

❖ The Norwegian National Criminal Police is considered among the leading law enforcement agencies in the world when it comes to investigation, intelligence and technological equipment to combat child pornography and abuse on the Internet.[14]

Resource

▶ Norwegian Association for Sexual and Reproductive Health (NSSR), RFSU Norge AS, Kirkegt. 5, 0152 Oslo, Norway. Tel: 47 (99) 35 92 73.

POLAND

Major Cities:	Warsaw, Lodz, Krakow
Ethnic Groups:	Polish 97%
Languages:	Polish (official) 98%
Major Religions:	Roman Catholic 90%
GDP per capita (PPP):	$20,900
Urban Population:	61%
Infant Mortality:	6 per 1,000 births
Life Expectancy:	Females: 81 years; Males: 73 years
Adult Literacy:	99%
Health Care System:	Hospitals, private physicians; 2 doctors per 1,000 people.

References
❏ *Reference World Atlas* (2013). NY: DK Publishing.
❏ *The World Almanac and Book of Facts 2013* (2012). NY: World Almanac Education Group.
❏ *The World Factbook https://www.cia.gov/library/publications/the-world-factbook/*

Sexual Activity

- The legal age of consent for sex is 15 years old.[1]
- Only 12% of young women surveyed said they began having sex before age 18.[2]

Contraception

- Contraception use is low due to the lack of availability.[3]
- Heavy church influences have caused pharmacists to give up stocking effective contraceptives.[3]
- A higher percentage of married women use national family planning and withdrawal (both accepted by the Catholic Church), as compared to other European women.[4]
- In Poland, sterilization as a method of family planning is illegal. Even with the written consent of the patient, sterilization is considered a criminal injury, which carries a penalty of up to 10 years in prison. Sterilization is legal only when performed upon "mentally incompetent individuals."[5]

Abortion

- In Poland, a liberalizing abortion law adopted in 1996 was invalidated by the Constitutional Court in 1997. The Court found that the law, which permitted abortion on social and economic grounds, violated the Constitution's protection of the right to life of the "conceived child." In December 1997, Poland's Parliament enacted new legislation eliminating social and economic grounds for abortion.[5]
- Currently, abortion in Poland is available on three grounds: when the pregnancy threatens the life or health of the woman; when there is justified suspicion that the pregnancy resulted from a "criminal act;" and in instances of fetal impairment.[5]

- The legal abortion rate is currently near zero as a consequence of new restrictions. Nevertheless, many Poles reportedly seek abortion services in nearby countries or from illegal providers in Poland.[6]
- The Federation for Women and Family Planning estimates there are at least 200,000 illegal abortions carried out annually.[7]

Sex Education[8]

- Sex education is a politically sensitive and contentious issue.
- In 1994 a law obligated the government to provide sexuality education in schools. In practice it is not included or minimal information is provided.
- A book completed by the Board of Education: *Preparing for Family Life*, was met with opposition from sex educators due to its content supporting the church's view on abortion and contraception use.

HIV/AIDS[9]

- An estimated 35,000 people were living with HIV/AIDS in Poland in 2011. Most of the infections are seen in Warsaw, the Gdansk region and Katowice (south).
- Injecting drug users account for the majority (58%) of all reported HIV cases in Poland.
- IDUs are systematically screened in treatment centers, outpatient clinics and residential homes. All other groups are tested on a voluntary basis.
- In a survey of gay men, very few reported having had an HIV test. There is still stigma, reflected in the low number of those voluntarily identifying themselves as gay or bisexual; the number of infections in this subpopulation may therefore be underestimated.

LGBT issues[10]

* In April 1995 the Constitutional Committee of the Polish Parliament proposed that the anti-discrimination clause of the constitution include protection from discrimination on the grounds sexual orientation. However this proposal met strong opposition, particularly from the Roman Catholic Church. The constitution as finally approved by Parliament in March 1997 says: "Nobody can be discriminated against based on any ground in political, social or economical life."
* Same-sex relations were decriminalized in 1932, establishing an equal age of consent of 15 years regardless of the sexual orientation.
* There is no recognition of same-sex couples. Article 18 of the Polish Constitution (1997) restricts marriage to heterosexual couples: "The marriage is a relationship between woman and man, the family, motherhood and parenthood are under protection and care of Republic of Poland." That does not mean it forbids registered partnership between the people of the same sex, but certainly defines marriage as a heterosexual one.

Prostitution[11]

* Prostitution is completely unregulated. However, pimping and recruiting is illegal.
* In 2007, 70 traffickers were convicted for forced prostitution.

Pornography[12]

* As of 1998, pornography is legal to possess, except for the possession and production of child, animal, and scenes of violence/rape.
* Also illegal is showing pornography to those who do not want to see it, and to children under 15.

Resource

▶ Polish Federation of Women and Family Planning *http://www.federa.org.pl/*

PORTUGAL

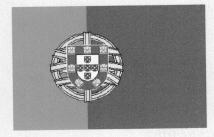

PORTUGAL

POPULATION: 10,799,270

CAPITAL: LISBON

Major Cities:	Lisbon, Porto
Ethnic Groups:	Homogeneous Mediterranean stock, small African minority
Languages:	Portuguese (official), Mirandese (official)
Major Religions:	Roman Catholic 85%
GDP per capita (PPP):	$23,800
Urban Population:	61%
Infant Mortality:	5 per 1,000 live births
Life Expectancy:	Females: 82 years; Males: 76 years
Adult Literacy:	95%
Health Care System:	National Health Services and private hospitals; 4 doctors per 1,000 people.

References

❑ *Reference World Atlas* (2013). NY: DK Publishing.

❑ *The World Almanac and Book of Facts 2013* (2012). NY: World Almanac Education Group.

❑ *The World Factbook https://www.cia.gov/library/publications/the-world-factbook/*

Sexual Activity

❖ The age of consent for heterosexual intercourse is 14, while homosexual sex is 16.[1]

Contraception

❖ Portugal has the second highest teen pregnancy rate in the European Union.[2]
❖ Condoms are the most popular method, followed by the pill. However, contraception use is inconsistent.[2]
❖ Emergency contraception is available over-the-counter.[3]

Abortion[4]

❖ Under current law a woman can have an abortion only if her life is in danger, to protect her mental or physical health, or in cases of rape, incest or fetal impairment.
❖ The restrictive abortion legislation in Portugal leaves many women who want to end an unwanted pregnancy with the only option of back street abortion. Such restrictive legislation results in more women traveling to neighboring countries, or resorting to illegal abortion in Portugal, risking, not only prosecution, but their lives and their health.
❖ Every year about 1,000 Portuguese women are treated in hospitals because of post-abortion complications or incomplete abortions.

Sex Education[5]

❖ The law passed in 1984 gave the right to sex education and family planning in the school curriculum.
❖ In 1999, the government organized—for the first time—an inter-ministerial commission with the aim of producing a governmental program on sex education and family planning. This commission was integrated by the Health Ministry, the Education Ministry, the Justice Ministry and the Labor and Social Solidarity Ministry. In October 1999 this program was launched—the first time that any Portuguese government has had a public program on these matters.
❖ In 2005, the Ministry of Health revised the policies to include sexuality education in the broader context of health education. While mandatory, it is unclear what is covered in schools.

HIV/AIDS

❖ An estimated 48,000 people were living with HIV/AIDS in Portugal at the end of 2011.[6]
❖ Trend analysis of surveillance data reflects the diversity of the HIV/AIDS situation in the country, but young adults are most affected.[6]
❖ Prior to 2000, Portugal did not report HIV cases so analysis of the HIV epidemic is difficult.[6]
❖ Portugal has the highest HIV incidence rates in Western Europe, with injecting drug use accounting for almost 50% of HIV diagnoses.[7]

LGBT issues[8]

❖ In 2004, Portugal became the first country in Europe and (after Ecuador, Fiji and South Africa) the fourth worldwide to explicitly ban sexual orientation discrimination by constitutional legislation.
❖ In 2010, the Parliament of Portugal passed a bill to remove marriage discrimination and therefore allow same-sex marriage. At the same time, however, it rejected the proposal to allow entitlement of adoption by same-sex couples.
❖ During 1997 several major events irreversibly changed the Portuguese lesbian and gay community and gave it a degree of visibility not previously achieved. These included the first AIDS Candlelight Memorial March, the first Pride Festival, the first Gay and Lesbian Film Festival and the opening of the first gay and lesbian community centre.

Prostitution[9]

❖ Prostitution is legal in Portugal.
❖ Pimping and brothel ownership is illegal.

Pornography[10]

❖ The legal age for viewing pornography in Portugal is 18.
❖ Hardcore pornography can only be shown in cinemas, not on TV.

Resource

▶ Associacao Para o Planeamento da Familia (APF) *http://www.apf.pt/*

ROMANIA

Major Cities:	Bucharest, Constana
Ethnic Groups:	Romanian 90%, Hungarian 7%, Roma 3%
Languages:	Romanian (official), Hungarian, German
Major Religions:	Eastern Orthodox 87%, Protestant 8%, Roman Catholic 5%
GDP per capita (PPP):	$13,000
Urban Population:	53%
Infant Mortality:	10 per 1,000 births
Life Expectancy:	Females: 78 years; Males: 71 years
Adult Literacy:	98%
Health Care System:	2 doctors per 1,000 people.

References
- *Reference World Atlas* (2013). NY: DK Publishing.
- *The World Almanac and Book of Facts 2013* (2012). NY: World Almanac Education Group.
- *The World Factbook https://www.cia.gov/library/publications/the-world-factbook/*

Sexual Activity

❖ The legal age of consent for sex is 15.[1]

Contraception

❖ Modern contraceptives are only sporadically available at a cost similar to abortion.[2]
❖ Reproductive services are mostly controlled by underpaid state-employed gynecologists.[2]
❖ Due to the lack of modern contraceptives, fears of their side effects and limited access to family planning services, women tend to rely on natural methods of birth control and abortion.[2]
❖ Romania has one of the highest rates of teen mothers in Europe.[3]

Abortion

❖ Abortion was legally available from 1957 to 1966, then was severely restricted as part of an overall pronatalist policy. As illegal and unsafe abortions replaced legal procedures, abortion-related mortality rose steeply, with 87% of maternal deaths attributed to unsafe abortions; just one year later, when most restrictions were removed, the rate fell to about one-third its peak level.[4]
❖ As of 1989 the new government of Romania abolished the law that prohibited abortions.[4]
❖ Many Romanian women accept abortions as a primary form of contraception due to their misconceptions about other forms of birth control.[5]

Sex Education[6]

❖ Sex education was removed from the school system in the early 1980's.
❖ Few efforts to introduce sex and contraception education into the secondary schools have been met with opposition from teachers and parents.
❖ Many have never had a single class in sexuality issues.

HIV/AIDS[7]

❖ An estimated 16,000 people were living with HIV/AIDS in Romania at the end of 2011.
❖ Most probably, Romania has the highest number of HIV infections in the sub-region of Central and South Eastern Europe.
❖ In 1989 a dramatic epidemic of HIV infection was discovered among orphans and hospitalized children who contracted HIV through blood transfusions.
❖ HIV testing is mandatory for STI and TB patients, pregnant women and prostitutes.
❖ Data on diagnosed HIV cases are reported at national level since 1992.

LGBT issues[8]

❖ Until November 14, 1996 same-sex relationships in Romania were illegal under Article 200 of the penal code. On that date Article 200 was amended so that the complete ban was lifted, but replaced with provisions that were almost as oppressive and discriminatory. Little real progress had been achieved.
❖ Sex-sex relations are legal except in cases where it causes a "public scandal," involves a minor, a defenseless person, or if it is by coercion or rape; up to five years in prison.
❖ Today in Romania, gays and lesbians are routinely denied some of the most basic human rights guaranteed by international law. Despite amendments in 1996 to the criminal code provisions relating to homosexual conduct—portrayed by the Romanian government as a total repeal of legislation criminalizing consensual sexual relations between adults of the same sex—gays and lesbians continue to be arrested and convicted for such relations if they become public knowledge.

Moreover, they face frequent physical abuse and harassment by law enforcement officials, as well as systematic discrimination in many walks of life. Romanian law not only prohibits private sexual acts between consenting adults of the same sex, but may also be interpreted to punish speech and association that expresses a homosexual identity—or even support of such identity.

❖ In 2012, the government presented legislation to affirm that marriage is only between a man and a woman.

Prostitution[9]

❖ Prostitution is illegal.
❖ Child prostitution is a problem due to the large number of unwanted children. Under dictator Nicolae Ceausescu, abortion was illegal, contraceptives unavailable, and sex education non-existent.

Pornography[10]

❖ Pornography is legal for those over 18.
❖ Magazines sold in stores must be wrapped in plastic.

Resource

▶ Society for Education in Contraception & Sexuality (SECS) *http://www.sexdex.ro/*

RUSSIAN FEDERATION

Major Cities:	Moscow, St. Petersburg, Nizhniy Novgorod, Novosibirsk
Ethnic Groups:	Russian 80%, Tatar 4%, Ukranian 2%
Languages:	Russian (official), many others
Major Religions:	Russian Orthodox 15–20%, Muslim 10–15%
GDP per capita (PPP):	$18,000
Urban Population:	74%
Infant Mortality:	8 per 1,000 births
Life Expectancy:	Females: 76 years; Males: 64 years
Adult Literacy:	99%
Health Care System:	4 doctors per 1,000 people

References
❑ *Reference World Atlas* (2013). NY: DK Publishing.
❑ *The World Almanac and Book of Facts 2013* (2012). NY: World Almanac Education Group.
❑ *The World Factbook https://www.cia.gov/library/publications/the-world-factbook/*

Sexual Activity[1]

❖ The legal age of consent is 16 years old.

Contraception

❖ Historically, abortion had been the main method of birth control because of the lack of choices.[2]
❖ An examination of contraceptive use from 1994 to 2003 found that 25% of sexually active Russian women had failed to use any contraceptive in the last month. The use of contraceptives did not increase across the decade.[2]
❖ The most common reasons for non-use were irregular sexual relations, desire to be pregnant, concern that contraceptives were uncomfortable, health problems, and the wide availability of abortion.[2]
❖ The most popular method of contraception is the IUD, used by 30% of women.[3]
❖ Emergency Contraception has been available for decades. Postinor is packaged in a 4-pill strip with directions for women to take one tablet immediately after intercourse, but to use no more than four tablets per month.[4]

Abortion

❖ The Russian Federation was the world's first country to legalize abortion. In 1920 the Communist Party legalized abortion in an attempt to destroy the traditional family and religion, and to create a new social basis for Russian Communist society. However, in 1936 the law was repealed and abortion was illegal. Abortion became legal again in 1955.[5]
❖ A decree issued in 2003 restricts the circumstances under which women may legally obtain abortions from the end of the 12th week until the beginning of the 22nd week of pregnancy. The decree reduces from 12 to 4 the number of conditions under which abortion is legal during this period.[6]

❖ Illegal abortion is still common; the number of illegal abortions is thought to equal the number of legal abortions.[6]
❖ The Russian Federation ranks second in the world to Romania in the number of abortions per capita. Girls in Russia (under 18) account for every tenth abortion. About 60% of all pregnancies in the Russian Federation end in abortion.[7]
❖ On average every woman born in Russia has two or three abortions.[7]
❖ RU-486 (Mifepristone) was approved for use in 2000.[8]

Sex Education[9]

❖ Sex education does not exist in the school curriculum. The Family Planning Association is the main agency involved in sex education.
❖ The federal program entitled "Principles of Family Planning and a Healthy Way of Life" for adolescents—developed by the Russian Family Planning Association and approved by the Minister of General and Professional Education and the Ministry of Health—was banned and deprived of funding as a result of political uproar. Opponents of sex education argued that sex education and the dissemination of contraceptives would corrupt and exterminate the Russian people.

HIV/AIDS

❖ An estimated 730,000-1.3 million people were living with HIV/AIDS in the Russian Federation at the end of 2011.[10]
❖ The Russian Federation has the biggest AIDS epidemic in all of Europe and one of the highest percentages of HIV-infected people in the world outside sub-Saharan Africa.[11]
❖ Russia currently does not accept funding from the Global Fund to Fight AIDS because it does not want to follow international protocols, such as dispensing clean needles.

LGBT issues

❖ In 1993 the Russian Parliament enacted a new penal code which no longer includes the prohibition of same-sex relations. Until 1993 consensual anal intercourse between adult males was punishable under Article 121.1 of the Russian Federation criminal code by imprisonment of up to five years. Lesbian relations were not criminalized.[12]

❖ Negative attitudes about LGBT persons persist, and no laws exist to protect against discrimination and harassment.[12]

❖ In 2012, Moscow banned gay pride marches for the next 100 years.[13]

❖ In 2013, Russia's parliament passed a bill that stigmatizes gay people and bans giving children any information about LGBT issues. Human rights groups around the world have called for a repeal since this type of law is a violation of basic human rights. Russia is also considering banning citizens from any country that allows same-sex marriage from adopting.[14]

❖ Russia is set to host the 2014 Winter Olympics. However, after passage of the anti-gay law, protests and threats of boycott have arisen from countries around the world.[15]

Prostitution[16]

❖ In 1987, the Supreme Soviet of the Russian Republic made prostitution illegal.

❖ Historically, the Soviet attempt to eradicate prostitution in the 1920s, by encouraging female employment, job-training, and government clinics and housing, is still considered more progressive than the alternatives used in many countries around the world today of regulation, prosecution, or decriminalization.[16]

Pornography

❖ The collapse of communism in the former USSR brought about a resurgence of commercially available sexually explicit materials. The problem became so acute that Prime Minister Mikhail Gorbachev appointed a committee to suggest measures to safeguard Russian morality.[17]

❖ Moscow authorities banned the sale of highly profitable erotic material on the Russian capital's streets and in transit stations. To protect children from pornography, which was rare in the former Soviet Union until the mid 1980s, the city council restricted sales of adult publications to designated shops and ordered sexually explicit materials wrapped in plastic to prevent perusal by minors. It also made illegal the sale of pornography to and by anyone under 16.[18]

Resources

▶ Russian Family Planning Association
   http://www.rfpa.ru/

▶ Russian Sexological Association, Krylatskiye Kholmy, 30-2, 207 Moscow.

RWANDA

RWANDA

POPULATION: 10,746,311

CAPITAL: **KIGALI**

Major Cities:	Kigali, Butare, Byumba, Kibeho, Nyanza
Ethnic Groups:	Hutu (Bantu) 84%, Tutsi (Hamitic) 15%, Twa (Pygmy) 1%
Languages:	Kinyarwanda, French and English (official) Swahili
Major Religions:	Roman Catholic 57%, Protestant 26%, Adventist 11%, Muslim 5%
GDP per capita (PPP):	$1,000
Urban Population:	18%
Infant Mortality:	67 per 1,000 births
Life Expectancy:	Females: 58 years; Males: 55 years
Adult Literacy:	70%
Health Care System:	1 physician per 20,000 people.

References

❏ *Reference World Atlas* (2013). NY: DK Publishing.
❏ *The World Almanac and Book of Facts 2013* (2012). NY: World Almanac Education Group.
❏ *The World Factbook https://www.cia.gov/library/publications/the-world-factbook/*

Sexual Activity[1]

❖ The legal age of consent is 18 years old.

Contraception

❖ The culture had always been strongly pronatalist; a traditional wedding toast encourages newly married couples, "Be fruitful, may you have many sons and daughters." And the Catholic Church has been a vocal critic and barrier to family planning. But in this context, President Kagame has declared family planning a national priority. In the words of the minister of health, "Family planning is priority number one—not just talking about it, but implementing it."[2]

❖ The contraceptive prevalence rate fell after the 1994 genocide, from 13% in 1992 to only 4% in 2000. By 2005, the rate had increased to the point where 10% of married women were using modern contraception. By 2008, indicate use among married women had increased to 27%.[2]

❖ Currently Rwanda is facing overwhelming consequences of its civil war, which led to the death of more than 500,000 people and a massive exodus from the country. The main challenge is to rebuild the health and family planning infrastructure so as to restore the accessibility of services.[3]

Abortion[3]

❖ Abortion was illegal until 1977. At that time, the law was expanded to allow some exceptions; the law prohibits abortion except when the continuance of the pregnancy seriously endangers the health of the pregnant woman. In such cases, a second medical opinion is required, and the intervention must be performed by a State physician or physician approved by the State in a public hospital or a private hospital approved by the State.

❖ Any person who induces an abortion is subject to 5–10 years' imprisonment if the woman does not consent and to two to five years' imprisonment if she consents.

Sex Education[4]

❖ Sex education is very limited. Most youth get information from their peers. There are efforts to educate youth on condom use due to the alarming rate of HIV in Rwanda.

HIV/AIDS

❖ An estimated 210,000 people were living with HIV/AIDS at the end of 2011.[5]

❖ Hundreds of thousands of women were brutally gang-raped as part of a systematic policy during the Rwandan genocide, with nearly two-thirds of the survivors contracting HIV as a result.[6]

LGBT issues[7]

❖ Homosexuality is not illegal, although provisions were introduced as recently as 2009 to criminalize homosexuality.

Prostitution[8]

❖ Prostitution is illegal in Rwanda.

❖ Many women are forced into prostitution due to poverty and it has added to the number of people living with HIV/AIDS in the country due to low condom use; 25% of prostitutes are estimated to be HIV positive.

Pornography

❖ No information available.

Resource

▶ Association Rwandaise pour le Bien-Etre Familial ARBEF, BP 1580 Kigali, Rwanda
Tel: 517138/572828

SINGAPORE

SINGAPORE
POPULATION: 5,460,302

CAPITAL: **SINGAPORE**

Major Cities:	Singapore
Ethnic Groups:	Chinese 77%, Malay 14%, Indian 8%
Languages:	Mandarin 35%, English 23%, Malay 14%, Hokkien 11%, Cantonese 6%, Teochew 5%. Tamill 3%
Major Religions:	Buddhist 43%, Muslim 15%, Christian 10%, Taoist 9%, Catholic 5%, Hindu 4%
GDP per capita (PPP):	$61,400
Urban Population:	100%
Infant Mortality:	2 per 1,000 live births
Life Expectancy:	Females: 87 years; Males: 82 years
Adult Literacy:	93%
Health Care System:	One of the highest health standards in Southeast Asia; 2 doctors per 1,000 people.

References

- *Reference World Atlas* (2013). NY: DK Publishing.
- *The World Almanac and Book of Facts 2013* (2012). NY: World Almanac Education Group.
- *The World Factbook https://www.cia.gov/library/publications/the-world-factbook/*

Sexual Activity

❖ The legal age of consent for heterosexual sex is 16; male same-sex relations are illegal.[1]
❖ In the early 1970's, Singapore attempted to reduce its population through national programs, including financial incentive for sterilization. By 1984, this was working too well, and by 1987, the birth shortfall was judged to be detrimental to the country. Sterilization incentives were no longer available to better-educated families, although it was retained for less-educated families, as well as those with three or more children. Three children were seen as the optimal family size. Advertising reflected this view.[2]
❖ Lee Kuan Yew, Singapore's founding leader suggested that polygamy may be a solution to one of Singapore's major problems: better educated women are less likely to marry and procreate, leaving the less educated women to have the majority of Singapore's offspring.[3]

Contraception

❖ The government, as part of its national development program, embarked on a family planning program immediately after Singapore achieved full independence in 1965. Besides the comprehensive provision of clinic services, the program included a wide range of social and fiscal incentives to achieve a "two child" family norm. After a decade of below replacement fertility, the government replaced the policy in 1987 with a selectively pro-natalist "three or more if you can afford it" policy.[4]
❖ Contraceptive services are readily available to the whole population through services provided by the Ministry of Health, public and private doctors.[4]
❖ About 60% of married couples report using some method of birth control. Condoms are the most common method used, followed by sterilization. The Pill and IUD are not popular methods.[5]

Abortion[6]

❖ Abortion was legalized in 1970, and was completely liberalized in 1975. This has led to the abolition of criminal abortions, allowing any woman access to a safer procedure.
❖ Ninety-five percent of all abortions are performed before the 13th week of pregnancy.
❖ Seventy-two percent of all abortions are performed on married women.
❖ Abortion ends about one third of all pregnancies in Singapore.

Sex Education

❖ The Singapore Planned Parenthood Association has an established formal sex education program in schools and also provides sex education for out-of-school youth.[4]
❖ A government program started in 2001, teaches sex and sexuality in school to 11-to-18-year-olds. Teenagers in secondary school discuss kissing in public, having sex, homosexuality, getting pregnant, pornography, and the dangers of sexually transmitted infection. Sexual harassment is also among the issues older teens discuss.[7]
❖ Mindful of differing views on sexuality, the government consulted major religious groups, as well as teachers, parents, students, psychologists and counselors before beginning the program. While students are given the facts on underage sex and LGBT issues, they are also told that these are against the law.[7]

HIV/AIDS[8]

❖ An estimated 3,400 people were living with HIV/AIDS in Singapore at the end of 2011.
❖ HIV testing among sex workers has been conducted in Singapore since 1985.

LGBT issues

❖ Same-sex relations are outlawed in Singapore.[3]

❖ Two sections of the Singapore Penal Code criminalize same-sex acts: Section 377 (Unnatural Offences): "Whoever voluntarily has carnal intercourse against the order of nature with any man, woman or animal, shall be punished with imprisonment for life, or with imprisonment for a term which may extend to ten years, and shall also be liable to fine. Penetration is sufficient to constitute the carnal intercourse necessary to the offence in this section." Section 377A (Outrages on Decency): "Any male person who, in public or private, commits, or abets the commission by any male person, of any act of gross indecency with another male person, shall be punished with imprisonment for a term which may extend to two years." Both sections carry a mandatory punishment of jail.[9]

❖ Visual representation of same-sex behavior is banned, and so are materials that portray being gay or lesbian as a legitimate and acceptable lifestyle.[9]

❖ In June 2013, over 20,000 people turned out for a "Pink Dot" rally in support of LGBT rights, indicating that Singapore may be moving to greater acceptance.[9]

Prostitution[10]

❖ Prostitution is legal, but operating a brothel and public soliciting are not. In Designated Red-light Areas (DRAs), it is officially tolerated.

❖ Working women must carry a yellow card stating that they are registered and have recently had a health exam.

❖ Some brothels provide benefits to keep employees.

❖ Prostitutes do not tend to work because of financial necessity, since there is no poverty and nearly full employment in Singapore.

Pornography[11]

❖ It is illegal to keep, distribute, or sell pornographic material. You can view pornography on the Internet, but it is illegal to download it.

❖ Sexually explicit material is censored by the Ministry of Information and the Arts.

❖ A Government-appointed panel determines what is banned from books, magazines, public, films, newspapers, etc. in Singapore.

Resource

▶ Singapore Planned Parenthood Association
http://www.sppa.org.sg/

SLOVAKIA

SLOVAKIA
POPULATION: 5,488,339

CAPITAL: BRATISLAVA

Major Cities:	Bratislava, Kosice
Ethnic Groups:	Slovak 86%, Hungarian 10%, Roma 2%
Languages:	Slovak (official) 84%, Hungarian 11%
Major Religions:	Roman Catholic 69%, Protestant 11%, Greek Catholic 4%
GDP per capita (PPP):	$24,000
Urban Population:	55%
Infant Mortality:	6 per 1,000 births
Life Expectancy:	Females: 80 years; Males: 72 years
Adult Literacy:	99%
Health Care System:	State health insurance, high immunization rates; 3 doctors per 1,000 people.

References
- *Reference World Atlas* (2013). NY: DK Publishing.
- *The World Almanac and Book of Facts 2013* (2012). NY: World Almanac Education Group.
- *The World Factbook https://www.cia.gov/library/publications/the-world-factbook/*

Sexual Activity

❖ The legal age of consent for sexual activity is 15 years old.[1]

Contraception

❖ Contraceptives in Slovakia are not covered by health insurance, making them inaccessible to many women and girls.[2]
❖ The lack of accurate, unbiased and comprehensive information on contraceptives further inhibits their access.[2]
❖ Only about 20% of women use the pill; 32% rely on withdrawal.[2]
❖ Due to the lack of use of reliable contraception methods, abortion has been the most reliable family planning practice.[2]
❖ The Slovak Family Planning Association is attempting to improve the public's knowledge about contraception, and to change negative attitudes.[3]
❖ The Slovak Family Planning Association is also attempting to introduce legislation on voluntary sterilization.[3]
❖ For decades, Postinor, an emergency contraceptive from Hungary, has been registered in Slovakia.[4]
❖ Emergency contraception is available without a prescription but is very expensive.[2]

Abortion[5]

❖ Abortion is available on request up to 12 weeks.
❖ It is also available in the second trimester for medical reasons, risk to the mother or the fetus, or for rape and other sexual crimes.
❖ There must be at least 6 months between abortions, with the exception of women with at least two births, aged 35 or more, or in the case of rape.
❖ Recommendation of physician is needed.
❖ Parental consent is required for minors under the age of 16; for women aged 16–18, a physician must inform parents after abortion.
❖ Counseling is required.

Sex Education

❖ Sexuality education in Slovakia is known as 'Education for Marriage and Parenthood' and has been mandatory since 1996.[6]
❖ It is not taught as a stand-alone subject but as part of either the Religion or Ethics curriculum.[6]
❖ The Catholic Church has played a role in hampering efforts to provide sexuality education, train teachers, and publish books on sexuality topics.[6]
❖ Family Planning Association is the main agency involved in sex education. It provides educational materials.[6]
❖ Slovakia's high abortion rate is attributed to inadequacies in school sex education.[3]
❖ Slovakia's Family Planning Association is working to influence public opinion about such topics through the use of mass media, and they are trying to create a comprehensive planned parenthood network.[3]

HIV/AIDS[7]

❖ Less than 500 people were estimated to be living with HIV/AIDS in Slovakia at the end of 2011.
❖ Well-designed national HIV/AIDS program are thought to have contributed to low prevalence among IDUs and low incidence in non-injecting populations. A syringe exchange program has been operating in Bratislava since 1994. The low prevalence of HIV in IDUs in the city is attributed to the success of the program.
❖ There has been a slow, but persistent increase of HIV + cases, mostly in MSM and heterosexuals.

LGBT issues[8]

❖ In 1990 a legal change signaled that same-sex and heterosexual behavior were to be treated equally when the age of consent became 15 years for same-sex and heterosexual behavior, and male prostitution was no longer regulated by the criminal law.

❖ Same-sex relationships are not recognized. A draft law that would give same-sex couples the status of "registered partners" has been ready since 1997.

❖ Slovakia's first gay pride parade was in 2010.

❖ In 2013, a law passed making homophobia illegal.

Prostitution[9]

❖ Prostitution is legal in Slovakia.

❖ Prostitution is larger and more organized than it was in 1989, at the end of Soviet rule.

❖ Inconsistent legislation allows the use of legal business premises for sexual services.

❖ The general feeling about prostitution is negative, and this attitude shows in a quote by Slovakian Interior Ministry member Tibor Shellberger: "We can say that prostitution today has become a very advantageous branch of international organized crime."

Pornography[10]

❖ Before 1989 pornographic materials were smuggled into the country from abroad. Now it is widely available and perfectly legal, not to mention that everything is on the internet.

Resource

▶ Slovak Association for Family Planning and Parenthood Education
http://www.rodicovstvo.sk/

SOUTH AFRICA

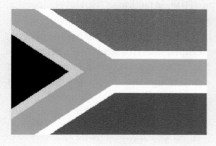

Major Cities:	Cape Town, Johannesburg, Pretoria
Ethnic Groups:	Black African 79%, White 10%, Colored 9%
Languages:	11 official languages including: IsiZulu, IsiXhosa, Sepedi, English, Setswanai, Sesotho, Xitsonja
Major Religions:	Protestant 37% (Zion Christian 11%, Pentacostal 8%, Methodist 7%, Dutch 7%, Anglican 4%), Catholic 7%
GDP per capita (PPP):	$11,600
Urban Population:	62%
Infant Mortality:	42 per 1,000
Life Expectancy:	Females: 49 years; Males: 50 years
Adult Literacy:	86%
Health Care System:	Private clinics, government supported programs; 1 doctor per 1,750 people.

References
❏ *Reference World Atlas* (2013). NY: DK Publishing.
❏ *The World Almanac and Book of Facts 2013* (2012). NY: World Almanac Education Group.
❏ *The World Factbook https://www.cia.gov/library/publications/the-world-factbook/*

Sexual Activity

❖ The legal age of consent is 16 years old.[1]
❖ The typical age of first intercourse: 16 years old.[2]
❖ Polygyny (multiple wives) is practiced by 15–30% of married men.[2]
❖ Among South Africans aged 15–24, more than half have had sex by age 18.[3]

Contraception

❖ In 1932, the government founded the Family Planning Association; it has 5,000 mobile sites that provide people with information and contraceptives.[4]
❖ Family Planning services are free of charge to all races.[4]
❖ Emergency contraception has been available without a prescription since 2001. Yet only one in four women surveyed reported having ever heard of it.[5]

Abortion

❖ South Africa enacted the Choice on Termination of Pregnancy Act in 1996, making its abortion law one of the most liberal in the world. The Act permits abortion without limitation as to reason during the first 12 weeks of pregnancy, within 20 weeks on numerous grounds and at any time if there is risk to the woman's life or of severe fetal impairment. The Act repealed a 1975 law that had prohibited abortion unless the pregnancy was a result of rape or incest, the mother's life was in danger, or there was a fetal impairment.[6]
❖ Legalization reduced the adverse consequences of unsafe abortion: Six months after legal abortion became available in February 1997, the number of incomplete abortions at one large hospital in Port Elizabeth had declined from an average of 18 every week to approximately four.[7]
❖ RU-486 (Mifepristone) is available for use in South Africa.[8]

Sex Education[9]

❖ Sexuality and HIV education has been offered in secondary schools in South Africa as part of the strategies for reducing HIV infections. However, several issues have been identified.

1) The content of the life skills curricula emphasize HIV and AIDS prevention information and awareness without providing the necessary life skills envisioned by the national policy, such as decision-making skills, the ability to develop healthy relationships and positive attitudes;

2) teachers and educators are not being provided with the training, guidance, support and resources that are essential for effective educational practices, and

3) the lack of community involvement is a barrier that limits the information flow to youths.

HIV/AIDS

❖ South Africa's epidemic is one of the worst in the world. Almost one in three pregnant women attending public antenatal clinics were living with HIV and trends show a gradual increase in HIV prevalence. There has been significant scale-up on the treatment front—around 190,000 people were receiving therapy by the end of 2005—however this still only represents less than 20% of those in need.[10]
❖ Nearly a million children have been orphaned by AIDS.[10]
❖ An estimated 5.6 million people (approx. 20% of adults) were living with HIV/AIDS in South Africa at the end of 2011—the world's largest population of people living with HIV.[11]
❖ Condom use at first intercourse has increased from 30% in 2002 to 65% in 2008.[11]
❖ In South Africa, as in many other developing countries, the primary method of HIV

transmission is heterosexual intercourse, and most South African youth know that HIV can be transmitted this way.[3]

LGBT issues

❖ The South African Constitution includes sexual orientation as a protected category.[12]

❖ On May 8, 1996 South Africa became the first country in the world to enshrine lesbian and gay rights in its Constitution: Clause 9 reads: "The state may not unfairly discriminate directly or indirectly against anyone on one or more grounds, including race, gender, sex, pregnancy, marital status, ethnic or social origin, color, sexual orientation, age, disability, religion, conscience, belief, culture, language, and birth." A similar provision had previously been included in the Interim Constitution adopted in December 1993. The ANC had formally recognized lesbian and gay rights as part of its policy at its conference in May 1992.[13]

❖ In 2005 same-sex unions were recognized.[13]

❖ In January 2000 the South African national assembly approved a bill that outlaws discrimination on grounds such as race, gender, religion and disability in a bid to eradicate the lingering inequalities of the apartheid era. The Promotion of Equality and Prevention of Unfair Discrimination Bill contains a wide-ranging list of 17 grounds on which no person may be discriminated against. These include sexual orientation, age, culture, pregnancy, marital status, conscience, social standing and language. Though already enshrined in the country's liberal 1996 constitution, they can now be enforced through every court in the country and replace the old regime's racist laws which were wiped off the statute books nearly a decade ago.[13]

Prostitution[14]

❖ Prostitution is illegal, as is pimping and brothel ownership. However, it is widespread.

Pornography[15]

❖ Pornography is legal for those over 18, but hosting a pornographic website is not.

❖ In 1994, pictures of women's breast couldn't be published without covering her nipples. However, today explicit magazines showing women's breast are made available in supermarkets.

Resource

▶ Planned Parenthood Association of South Africa, Third Floor, Marlborough House, 60 Eloff, Johannesburg, So. Africa, 2001

SPAIN

Major Cities:	Madrid, Barcelona, Valencia, Seville, Zaragoza
Ethnic Groups:	Mix of Mediterranean and Nordic types
Languages:	Castilian Spanish (official) 74%, Catalan 17%, Galician 7%, Basque 2%
Major Religions:	Roman Catholic 94%
GDP per capita (PPP):	$31,100
Urban Population:	77%
Infant Mortality:	3 per 1,000
Life Expectancy:	Females: 85 years; Males: 78 years
Adult Literacy:	98%
Health Care System:	4 doctors per 1,000 people.

References

❑ *Reference World Atlas* (2013). NY: DK Publishing.

❑ *The World Almanac and Book of Facts 2013* (2012). NY: World Almanac Education Group.

❑ *The World Factbook* https://www.cia.gov/library/publications/the-world-factbook/

Sexual Activity

* The legal age of consent is 13; this is the lowest age of consent in Europe.[1]
* Typical age of first intercourse: 16.5 years old.[2]

Contraception

* Contraceptive use was officially legalized in 1978.[3]
* Emergency contraception is available without consulting a doctor or having a prescription.[4]
* In 2010, the Spanish senate approved a new law on sexual and reproductive health requiring that public policies related to health, education and social issues promote universal access to sexual and reproductive health services and programs—including family planning services.[5]

Abortion

* In 2010, the Spanish senate approved a new law on sexual and reproductive health, which relaxed restrictions on women's access to abortion. The law allows abortion under any circumstances at up to 14 weeks' gestation and declares the procedure a woman's right.[5]
* It also permits abortion at up to 22 weeks if two doctors certify that the pregnancy poses a serious threat to the woman's life or health, as well as in cases of fetal impairment, and beyond 22 weeks in cases of severe fetal impairment.[5]
* Previously, safe abortion was widely available in Spain, but was legal only to save the life of a woman, or to preserve her physical and mental health.[5]
* The new law grants 16- and 17-year-olds abortion access, provided that they notify at least one parent or legal guardian. Notification is not required if the teen believes it would result in

"domestic violence, threats, coercion, abuse, or a situation of uprooting or helplessness."[5]
* RU-486 (mifepristone) was approved for marketing in 1999.[6]

Sex Education

* Once a taboo subject, sexuality is now present on television, in cinema and in magazines, and it has been included in official education programs.[7]
* Spain is a Catholic country and statements of the Roman Catholic Church have had an effect on such issues as sexuality education. However, there is public acceptance of sexuality education.[7]
* Sexuality education has been available in schools since the 1970s, but there has been no mandated curriculum or required topics.[7]
* The new law on sexual and reproductive health passed in 2010 made comprehensive sexuality education mandatory in schools.[5]

HIV/AIDS

* An estimated 150,000 people were living with HIV/AIDS in Spain at the end of 2011.[8]
* Barcelona has a large LGBT population and a quarter of gay men in Barcelona are HIV positive.[9]
* In March 2013, Spanish researchers announced they had developed an HIV vaccine that reduces the level of the virus by 90%.[9]

LGBT issues

* The Spanish Penal Code declares the right to express one's sexual orientation as a fundamental freedom and bans discrimination based on sexual orientation in housing, employment, public services, and professional activities. It also criminalizes hatred and violent acts

against individuals based on their sexual orientation.[10]

❖ This Penal Code is one of the most advanced in penalizing discrimination based on sexual orientation, and the first to protect the rights of gay people in a Latin Catholic country.[11]

❖ The Spanish parliament approved a new law in 2005, which allows same-sex marriages and adoptions.[12]

Prostitution[13]

❖ Prostitution itself is legal, but several surrounding activities are not. Brothels were outlawed in 1956, but they live on in the form of "Clubs."

❖ Spain is known as the "brothel of Europe" with over 500,000 prostitutes.

Pornography[14]

❖ Pornography is legal for those over 18 and sold openly in most book stands.

Resources

▶ Federacion de Planificacion Familiar de Espana *http://www.fpfe.org/*

▶ Federacion Espanola de Sociedades de Sexologia, c/Valencians, 6-Principal, 46002, Valencia.

▶ Societat Catalan de Sexologia, Tren de Baix, 51, 20, 20, 08223 Teraessa, Barcelona.

▶ Sociedad Sexologica de Madrid, c/Barbieri, 33 dcha, 28004, Madrid.

SWEDEN

SWEDEN
POPULATION: 9,119,423

CAPITAL: STOCKHOLM

Major Cities:	Stockholm, Goteborg, Malmo, Uppsala
Ethnic Groups:	Swedish 89%, Finnish 2%
Languages:	Swedish (official)
Major Religions:	Lutheran 87%
GDP per capita (PPP):	$41,900
Urban Population:	85%
Infant Mortality:	3 per 1,000 live births
Life Expectancy:	Females: 84 years; Males: 79 years
Adult Literacy:	99%
Health Care System:	4 doctors per 1,000 people

References
❑ *Reference World Atlas* (2013). NY: DK Publishing.
❑ *The World Almanac and Book of Facts 2013* (2012). NY: World Almanac Education Group.
❑ *The World Factbook https://www.cia.gov/library/publications/the-world-factbook/*

Sexual Activity

* The legal age of consent is 15 years old.[1]
* Sweden has very liberal attitudes towards teenage sexuality.[2]
* There are no parental rights when it comes to the sexuality of minors, except below the age of 15. A young Swedish girl can independently decide whether she wants to have a boyfriend, have sex with him, have contraceptives or even have an abortion.[2]
* The typical age of first intercourse is 16.[3]

Contraception

* Contraceptives are easily accessible, affordable and available to anyone, regardless of age or marital status. Such accessibility has proven effective in the prevention of teen pregnancy. For example, only 35 babies were born to teens under 16 in 1993.[2]
* Youth Clinics in every community offer free, confidential services and counseling in sexual matters to young people.[2]
* Contraception was legalized in 1938.[4]
* Anyone who is over 25 and a Swedish citizen or legal resident can be sterilized on request.[4]
* Birth control pills are free for the first 3 months.[5]
* Since 1990, the RFSU clinic has advocated emergency contraception by offering the service and information to both professionals and the general public.[6]

Abortion

* Sweden has one of the lowest numbers of abortions in the world.[2]
* Available on request up to 12 weeks on consultation with a doctor, between 12 and 18 weeks on consultation with a doctor and a counselor, and after 18 weeks with the approval of the National Board of Health and Welfare.[4]
* Abortion is free up to the 18th week.[5]
* RU 486 (Mifepristone) has been available since 1992.[7]
* More then half (51%) of abortions performed within 63 days of a woman's last menstrual period use Mifepristone/RU 486.[8]

Sex Education

* Sex education has been a compulsory subject in Swedish schools since 1955. Sex education starts at the age of seven, in the first grade, and then is brought up on a recurring basis for approximately 15 hours per year.[9]
* Swedish children receive their first sex education at home, from their parents.
* Sex education is well integrated in school curricula.[9]
* Swedish sex education has been based on the principles of democracy, tolerance, and human equality. Ethical principles of Swedish sex education include: (a) Nobody is entitled to regard and treat another human being simply as a means of selfish gratification, (b) Mental pressure and physical force are always a violation of individual liberty, and (c) Sexuality forming part of a personal relationship has more to offer than casual sex and is therefore worth aspiring to.[10]

HIV/AIDS[11]

* An estimated 9,100 people were living with HIV/AIDS in Sweden at the end of 2011.
* HIV testing is mandatory for blood donors and systematic but voluntary for pregnant women, women having abortions, IDU, STI patients, immigrants, refugees and deceased with autopsies.
* All diagnosed HIV infections are registered in the Swedish national HIV case reporting system, using an identifying code.

* During the 1990s the Swedish HIV-epidemic has been influenced by the global epidemic. People who have been infected outside Sweden, usually in countries with a generalized epidemic, contribute 2/3 of the reported cases in recent years. The majority of this group has been infected prior to their immigration to Sweden.

LGBT issues

* The Partnership Act was passed in 1994. This meant that same-sex couples that contract a partnership with each other had broadly the same rights as heterosexual couples who contract a marriage with each other. There were some exceptions, for example, same-sex couples were not allowed to adopt children.[12]
* In 2003, Sweden allowed LGBT couples to adopt.[12]
* In 1972, Sweden became the first country to allow transgender people to legally change their gender.[12]

* In 2009, Sweden became the seventh country in the world to legalize same-sex marriage.[13]
* In 2012, Sweden adopted the gender neutral pronoun "hen."[14]

Prostitution[15]

* In Sweden it is legal to sell sex, but it is illegal to be a pimp and since 1999 also to buy sexual services. The reason for this law is to protect prostitutes, as many of them have been forced into prostitution by someone or by economic necessity. Prostitutes are generally viewed by the government as oppressed, while their clients are viewed as oppressors.

Pornography[16]

* In Sweden, there are no age laws for possession or viewing of pornography. The possession of child pornography is forbidden but it is not forbidden to "watch."

Resources

▶ Swedish Association for Sex Education (RFSU) *http://www.rfsu.se/*

▶ Swedish National Institute of Public Health *http://www.fhi.se/en/*

SWITZERLAND

SWITZERLAND
POPULATION: 7,996,026

CAPITAL: BERN

Major Cities:	Zurich, Basel, Geneva, Lausanne
Ethnic Groups:	German 65%, French 18%, Italian 10%, Romansch 1%
Languages:	German 64%, French 20%, Italian 7% (all official)
Major Religions:	Roman Catholic 42%, Protestant 35%
GDP per capita (PPP):	$46,200
Urban Population:	74%
Infant Mortality:	4 per 1,000 births
Life Expectancy:	Females: 85 years; Males: 80 years
Adult Literacy:	99%
Health Care System:	Excellent, major producer of specialized pharmaceutical products; 4 doctors per 1,000 people.

References

❑ *Reference World Atlas* (2013). NY: DK Publishing.
❑ *The World Almanac and Book of Facts 2013* (2012). NY: World Almanac Education Group.
❑ *The World Factbook https://www.cia.gov/library/publications/the-world-factbook/*

Sexual Activity

❖ The legal age of consent in Switzerland is 16 years old.[1]
❖ Nearly 40% of women surveyed said they began having sex before age 18.[2]
❖ The age of first intercourse is essentially the same as other European countries.[3]
❖ Switzerland has one of the lowest teen pregnancy rates. This seems to be the result of widespread Swiss school sexuality education programs and a nationwide AIDS campaign that has stressed the use of condoms in sexual activities.[3]

Contraception

❖ Condom use is high among teen. Most (87%) report using condoms at first intercourse.[3]
❖ High school students were the ones who requested condom availability in schools.[4]
❖ There are numerous family planning centers throughout the country, some for counseling only, but others offering gynecological exams and contraception.[4]
❖ Adolescents can easily obtain birth control.[4]
❖ In 2010, Switzerland started selling "The Hotshot" an adolescent-sized condom for boys 12–14 in an attempt to increase safe sex.[5]

Abortion

❖ Abortion has been legal since 1942.[4]
❖ In June 2002, the Swiss public voted for abortion on request of the woman within the first 12 weeks of pregnancy.[6]
❖ Young women under the age of 16 have to visit a counseling centre before an abortion can be performed.[6]
❖ The costs of the abortion is covered by health insurance.[6]
❖ RU-486 (Mifepristone) was approved for marketing in 1999.[7]

Sex Education

❖ Switzerland has a long history of school-based sex education.[3]
❖ In 2011, a controversy occurred over the introduction of "sex boxes" distributed by the Department of Education to elementary school teachers in Basel, Switzerland. The boxes were designed to assist teachers in covering sexuality education topics and included activities, puzzles, and a penis and vagina model.[8]

HIV/AIDS[9]

❖ An estimated 20,000 people were living with HIV/AIDS in Switzerland at the end of 2011.
❖ A major focus is on men who have sex with men.
❖ The countries national AIDS prevention campaign is Love Life Stop AIDS.

LGBT issues

❖ In 1992 referendums in Switzerland were held. One of the results was that the age of consent for same-sex sexual activity was no longer different from that of heterosexuals.[10]
❖ In 1995, a petition was brought to the Parliament by the national gay and lesbian organization, Pink Cross, seeking partnership rights for homosexuals; the right to register one's partnership was passed in 1996.[10]
❖ Registered partnerships have been recognized since 2007.[10]
❖ In 2012, same-sex couples were allowed to adopt each other's children.[11]
❖ A transgender person is free to change their gender on legal documents.[10]

Prostitution[12]

❖ Prostitution is legal, and prostitutes must register with the authorities. They are considered self-employed.

❖ In certain areas, street prostitution is banned.

❖ In 2013, in an effort to reduce open street prostitution and to make it safer for sex workers, Zurich introduced "sex drive-ins."

Pornography[13]

❖ Pornography is legal, but subject to exceptions (e.g., must be 16). Hard pornography, dealing with children, animals, excrement or violence is illegal.

Resource

▶ PLANes—Fondation Suisse pour la Santé Sexuelle et Reproductive
http://www.plan-s.ch/

THAILAND

Major Cities:	Bangkok, Nakhon, Ratchasima, Chiang Mai
Ethnic Groups:	Thai 75%, Chinese 14%
Languages:	Thai (official), English
Major Religions:	Buddhist 95%; Muslim 4%
GDP per capita (PPP):	$10,300
Urban Population:	34%
Infant Mortality:	15 per 1,000 live births
Life Expectancy:	Females: 77 years; Males: 72 years
Adult Literacy:	93%
Health Care System:	< 1 doctor per 1,000 people; volunteer health organizations, private market government, hospitals, government health centers, traditional healers.

References

❏ *Reference World Atlas* (2013). NY: DK Publishing.

❏ *The World Almanac and Book of Facts 2013* (2012). NY: World Almanac Education Group.

❏ *The World Factbook https://www.cia.gov/library/publications/the-world-factbook/*.

Sexual Activity

❖ The legal age of consent is 15 years old.[1]

❖ There has been a cultural shift in the past two decades leading to greater acceptability of premarital sex among young women.[2]

❖ Public discussion of sexuality-related topics is considered a societal taboo.[2]

❖ Men have more sexual freedom than women; this is not only permitted but expected.[2]

Contraception

❖ Oral contraceptives, injectables and IUDs have helped slow the population growth of Thailand.[3]

❖ In July 1997, Thailand released a National Reproductive Health Policy statement reinforcing that "All Thai citizens at all ages must have good reproductive health throughout their entire lives."[3]

❖ Extended network ties affect contraceptive choice. The more external kinship ties households have, the more likely women in those households are to use modern forms of contraception.[4]

❖ Emergency contraceptives are available over the counter and where non-pharmacists are allowed to dispense medications.[5]

Abortion[6]

❖ Abortion is technically illegal except in cases of rape or threat to the woman's health.

❖ Two-thirds of women who experience unplanned pregnancies seek abortion from an abortionist who is not medically trained.

Sex Education[3]

❖ Sex education has been introduced in the school curricula in 1978, 1981 and more recently has been revised in 2001 within the broader context of reproductive health and sexuality, HIV/AIDS, safe sex, contraceptive use, pregnancy and parenthood.

❖ The Government has developed materials on sex education and educated parents on sexuality equipping them to discuss issues of sex and sexuality with their children.

❖ In March 2005, the Ministry of Education launched its first sex education guidebook to be used in a pilot in some 20 to 30 primary and secondary schools. It provides tips on how teachers should educate students on sexuality issues. The guidebook covers six areas—sexual development, interpersonal relationships, prevention of sexual harassment, sexual behavior, sex-related health issues, and sex within the society and cultural context.

HIV/AIDS

❖ An estimated 490,000 people were living with HIV/AIDS in Thailand at the end of 2011.[7]

❖ Prevention efforts have resulted in declining levels of HIV since the late 1990s as fewer men bought sex and condom use rates rose. However, recent studies show that premarital sex has become more commonplace among young Thais and more than one-third of HIV infections in 2005 were among women who had been infected by their long-term partners.[7]

❖ In 1991, all government-sponsored sexually transmitted disease (STD) clinics began to promote condom use in the commercial sex setting. The "100% condom program" enlisted the cooperation of sex establishment owners and sex workers to encourage all clients to use condoms when obtaining sex. The government supplied almost 60 million free condoms a year to support this activity. For example, from 1989 to 1993, the use of condoms in commercial sex increased from 14% to 94%.[8]

LGBT issues

❖ While in general Thailand has one of the world's more liberal sexual cultures in terms of public tolerance of LGBT persons, pockets of intense homophobia do exist.[9]

❖ In 2012, legislation was introduced to legalize same-sex marriage. Although it did not pass, it is thought it will pass in the near future since Thailand is considered the most gay-friendly country in southeast Asia.[10]

❖ Katoeys or "ladyboys" refer to transgender women or an effeminate gay male; they are regarded by some as a third sex.[11]

Prostitution

❖ In 1960 the Prohibiting Prostitution Act was passed making prostitution, brothel keeping, and procurement illegal in Thailand.[12]

❖ During the Vietnam War, Thailand was the R&R center for the American troops. The sex industry was so well established that after the war ended Thailand had to attract an alternative clientele or disemploy thousands of workers.[13]

❖ Female sexuality plays a critical role in Thailand's economic development and growth.[5] Prostitution is looked at as a means to support the family and provide for basic material needs.[3]

❖ The commercial sex industry is ruled by the laws of economics. New money and changing tastes are bringing younger and younger girls and boys into the business. There is an estimated 100,000 children under the age of 18 working as prostitutes.[14]

Pornography[15]

❖ Possession of pornography for personal use is fine. Production, distribution and possession with an intent to show to the public is illegal.

TURKEY

TURKEY

POPULATION: 77,804,122

CAPITAL: **ANKARA**

Major Cities:	Istanbul, Ankara, Izmir, Adana
Ethnic Groups:	Turk 70–75%, Kurd 18%
Languages:	Turkish (official), Kurdish, Dimli, Azeri, Kabardian
Major Religions:	Muslim 99.8%
GDP per capita (PPP):	$15,200
Urban Population:	72%
Infant Mortality:	22 per 1,000 live births
Life Expectancy:	Females: 75 years; Males: 71 years
Adult Literacy:	87%
Health Care System:	1 doctor per 1,000 people; National Health Care system, government hospitals, health centers, health houses and the private health care market.

References

❑ *Reference World Atlas* (2013). NY: DK Publishing.
❑ *The World Almanac and Book of Facts 2013* (2012). NY: World Almanac Education Group.
❑ *The World Factbook* https://www.cia.gov/library/publications/the-world-factbook/

Sexual Activity

- The legal age of consent is 18 years old.[1]
- Illegal virginity tests were commonly conducted on unmarried women who were in police detention, or women who were applying for government jobs. These tests were also administered to "suspicious" female students in schools. As of 1995, the tests were no longer allowed to be given in schools.[2]
- Honor killings, the execution of a girl or woman to protect a family's reputation, are still a concern in Turkey and were the focus of a 2005 report by the United Nations.[3]

Contraception[4]

- Turkey, which has a history of progressive policies and legislation designed to improve maternal and child health, legalized family planning education and the provision of temporary contraceptive methods in the mid-1960s; legalization of abortion and sterilization followed later, in 1983.
- Turkey's family planning program is relatively advanced and has helped the country achieve a total contraceptive prevalence rate of 64%. There is still a high degree of reliance on traditional methods such as withdrawal.

Abortion

- Abortion became legal in 1983. Abortions are available on request up to 10 weeks; for over 10 weeks in cases of: risk to woman's life or risk to fetal health or handicap. A report from two specialists is needed in cases of risk to the woman's or fetus's health.[5]
- In 2012, the Prime Minister announced he would like to restrict abortion to the first few weeks of a pregnancy, at a time when most women do not realize they are pregnant.[5]

- Married women need consent from their husbands and minors need consent from parents, guardian or magistrate's court.[6]
- The inadequacy of family planning services for abortion clients, which leads to many women to go on to have repeat abortions, constitutes a major public health issue in Turkey.[4]
- Women turn to abortion because contraceptive options are not readily available. Once quality family planning services are made available to abortion clients, they accept family planning methods at high rates.[4]

Sex Education

- A Sex Education Task Force was established in 1997 by the Family Planning Association to convince the Ministry of National Education that sex education needs to become a priority.[7]
- The FPA broadcasts a weekly educational radio and TV program 'Healthy Family—Happy Society,' with audience feedback. It also runs personal and telephone helpline counseling services.[8]
- Despite the efforts of the Family Planning Association, there is little support for sexuality education. In fact, 95% of parents said they "never" want their children learning about sex in school.[9]

HIV/AIDS[10]

- Less than 5,500 people were estimated to be living with HIV/AIDS in Turkey at the end of 2011.
- HIV testing is mandatory for blood donors, prostitutes and military service conscripts abroad.
- All diagnosed HIV-infections are reported in a national HIV case reporting system.

* Turkey has a low level epidemic and commercial sex workers can be seen as the major driver.

LGBT issues

* Sisters of Venus, the first Turkish lesbian group was established in July 1994. It is helping to report on women's legal situation in Turkey, including a comprehensive report on lesbians' rights. They also provide educational material on AIDS for Turkish women.[11]
* The first Gay Pride parade was held in 2003 with a few dozen people; by 2013 there were over 20,000 in attendance.[12]
* In 2013, Turkey became the second major Muslim country (after Albania) to add protections to sexual minorities.[13]

Prostitution[14]

* Prostitution is legal but tolerated in Turkey.
* There are believed to be 15,000 registered sex workers; there are estimated to be 100,000 additional unregistered sex workers.
* Women from Romania and Russia come to Turkey to trade sexual favors to earn money for a legitimate business back home.
* There are both male and female brothels.
* Women who work in brothels must have legal licenses and are supervised by doctors and must be given a clean bill of health to work.

Pornography[15]

* Turkey was the first country to legally produce pornographic materials in the Muslim world.
* Modest editions of *Penthouse* and similar magazines are sold at newsstands, bolder ones in white cellophane covers.
* In 2004, legislation made it illegal to distribute obscene images, words, or texts.
* In 2006, the government banned the four erotic television channels.

Resources

▶ Family Planning Association of Turkey, Türkiye Aile Planlamasi Dernegi (TAPD), Cemal Nadir Sok. No:11 Çankaya/Ankara, Turkey. Tel: 90 (312) 441 78 00 / +90 (312) 441 79 00.

▶ Turkish Family Health & Planning Foundation, Sitesi A Blok D.3-4, 80660 Entiler, Istanbul, Turkey.

UNITED KINGDOM

UNITED KINGDOM
OF **GREAT BRITAIN** &
N. IRELAND
POPULATION: **63,395,574**

CAPITAL: **LONDON**

Major Cities:	In England (50 M): London 7.5 million
	In Scotland (5 M): Edinburgh 0.5 million
	In Wales (3 M): Cardiff: 0.3 million
	In N. Ireland (1.5 M): Belfast: 0.3 million
Ethnic Groups:	White 92%, Black 2%
Languages:	English, Welsh, Scottish form of Gaelic
Major Religions:	Christian (Anglican, Roman Catholic, Presbyterian, Methodist) 72%, Muslim 3%
GDP per capita (PPP):	$35,700
Urban Population:	80%
Infant Mortality:	5 per 1,000 births
Life Expectancy:	Females: 83 years; Males: 78 years
Adult Literacy:	99%
Health Care System:	National health care; 3 doctors per 1,000 people.

References:
- *Reference World Atlas* (2013). NY: DK Publishing.
- *The World Almanac and Book of Facts 2013* (2012). NY: World Almanac Education Group.
- *The World Factbook https://www.cia.gov/library/publications/the-world-factbook/.*

Sexual Activity

- ❖ The legal age of consent is 16 years old.[1]
- ❖ Typical age of first intercourse: 16 years old.[2]
- ❖ A comparison of Western and Northern Europe and the US shows that the UK has the highest teen birth and abortion rates in Western Europe, exceeded only by the US.[3]
- ❖ The teen birth rate in the UK is twice as high as in Germany and France, and five times as high as in The Netherlands.[3]
- ❖ In a study comparing teens in the UK to teens in The Netherlands about their reasons for having sexual intercourse for the first time, the teens in the UK were more likely to say it was due to peer pressure or opportunity, whereas teens in The Netherlands were much more likely to say it was due to love or commitment.[4]

Contraception

- ❖ Fifty-seven percent of 16–19 year olds use contraception.[5]
- ❖ Of those teens who use contraceptives, 65% said they used condoms and 54% said they used the Pill.[6]
- ❖ Since April 1974, all contraceptive advice provided by the NHS and all pre-scribed supplies were made available free of charge irrespective of age or marital status.[6]
- ❖ Health professionals can provide contraceptive advice and treatment to those under 16 without parental consent in certain circumstances.[7]
- ❖ Mirena, an IUD used widely in Scandinavia, was approved for use in the UK in 1995.[8]
- ❖ Emergency contraception has been available since 1983; however, a major public education campaign was launched in 1995.[9]
- ❖ Emergency contraception is now sold over the counter.[10]

Abortion

- ❖ Legal up to 24 weeks, with permission of 2 physicians; however, it is still illegal in Northern Ireland.[11]
- ❖ The majority of abortions (91%) take place within the first 12 weeks of pregnancy.[12]
- ❖ Most abortions are funded by the National Health Service.[12]
- ❖ Mifepristone/RU 486 has been available since 1991.[13]
- ❖ Medication abortions (RU486) account for nearly half (47%) of abortions.[12]

Sex Education[14]

- ❖ In England and Wales, sex education is required in secondary schools. The basic biology—puberty, where do babies come from, and so on—is part of the science national curriculum.
- ❖ Primary schools in England are required by law to have a policy on sex education. Secondary schools are required by law to make provision for sex education. Sex education is not fully defined by the law, but it must include education about HIV/AIDS and other STIs. Parents have a legal right to withdraw their children from sex education, except for those parts that are within the National Curriculum.
- ❖ In Scotland, jurisdiction over the provision of sex education lies with the local education authority. In Northern Ireland, sex education is not mandated, although it is encouraged in the teaching of health education.

HIV/AIDS

- ❖ An estimated 94,000 people had been diagnosed with HIV/AIDS in the United Kingdom at the end of 2011.[15]
- ❖ In 2011, around 48% were infected through heterosexual sex, and 48% through sex between men.[16]

- It is estimated that a quarter of people who are HIV+ do not know it.[16]
- The Terence Higgins Trust was the first organization in the UK to be set up in response to the HIV epidemic and is one of the oldest in the world.[17]

LGBT issues[18]

- Despite its thriving lesbian and gay community, highly effective lobbying organizations, and several "out" government ministers and Members of Parliament, the UK has had the most repressive legal situation of any country in Western Europe other than Cyprus. Discriminatory privacy, soliciting, and age of consent laws for gay men (until 2001); a ban on lesbian and gays in the armed forces (until 2000), resulting in an average of one dismissal every week; the notorious Section 28, which banned the "promotion of homosexuality" by local authorities, introduced during the Thatcher era in 1988 (until 2003); and no anti-discrimination policies (until 2010).
- Since 2005, same-sex couples are allowed to enter into civil partnerships, a separate union which provides the legal consequences of marriage.
- Transgender people have had the right to change their legal gender since 2005.

Prostitution

- Prostitution is technically legal, but several surrounding activities are outlawed which make it hard to work legally. For example, it is illegal to solicit or advertise, run a brothel, or curb-crawl.[19]
- So-called tart cards are cards found in phone booths in London, Hove and Brighton that advertise the services of call girls. They are typically placed in phone booths by professional "carders," who tour the phone booths, replacing cards which have been removed by the telephone companies' cleaners. Placing them in phone booths is illegal, although this has only reduced their number, rather than eliminating them.[20]
- The English Collective of Prostitutes is working to decriminalize prostitution.[21]

Pornography

- The major means of regulation of pornography have been through the *Customs Consolidation Act 1876* (which controls imports), the *Obscene Publications Act 1956* (publishing an obscene article for gain), and the *Indecent Displays Act 1981* (which makes it an offense to display in public material which is indecent or may cause offense or embarrassment to the public).[22]
- The Williams Committee of Great Britain was established in 1977 to review pornography; their conclusion that the effect of pornography was a nuisance rather than a harm provided the basis for its recommendation that the principal method of controlling pornography should be to restrict its availability, primarily so that children and young adults and those who had no interest in the material would be less likely to come in contact with it.[22]
- Specific legislation addressing the use of children in pornography is provided by the Protection of Children Act 1978 which makes it an offense to publish, distribute or take an indecent photo of a child, and the Criminal Justice Act 1988 which makes it an offense to possess an indecent photo of a child.[22]
- Viewing Internet child pornography means committing an offense.[23]
- In 2013, British Internet providers agreed to put adult-content filters on phones, public WI-FI networks and home computers. The filter can be deactivated by those who can prove they are 18 or older.[24]

Resources

▶ Family Planning Association of the UK *http://www.fpa.org.uk/*

▶ Sex Education Forum, National Children's Bureau *http://www.sexeducationforum .org.uk/*

UNITED STATES

UNITED STATES

POPULATION: 316,668,567

CAPITAL: **WASHINGTON, DC**

Major Cities:	New York, Los Angeles, Chicago, Houston, Philadelphia
Ethnic Groups:	White 80%; Black 13%, Asian 4%
Languages:	English (official) 82%, Spanish 11%
Major Religions:	Protestant 51%, Catholic 24%, Mormon 2%, Jewish 2%, Muslim <1%
GDP per capita (PPP):	$50,700
Urban Population:	82%
Infant Mortality:	6 per 1,000 births
Life Expectancy:	Females: 81 years; Males: 76 years
Adult Literacy:	99%
Health Care System:	Private physicians, publicly funded clinics; no national health insurance; 3 doctors per 1,000 people.

References

❏ *Reference World Atlas* (2013). NY: DK Publishing.
❏ *The World Almanac and Book of Facts 2013* (2012). NY: World Almanac Education Group.
❏ *The World Factbook https://www.cia.gov/library/publications/the-world-factbook/*.

Sexual Activity

❖ The legal age of consent for sex varies from state to state, however for most states it is 16 years of age.[1]

❖ Typical age of first intercourse: 16–17 years old; most young people begin having sex in their mid to late teens, about 8 years before they marry.[2]

❖ Although rates of teen births in the U.S. are at their lowest level in the 6 decades for which data exist, this rate is still higher than other industrialized countries.[3]

❖ Compared to other countries such as Canada, Sweden, France, and Great Britain, the U.S. has the highest rates of teen pregnancies, births, abortions, and STIs, and a higher proportion of teens report no contraceptive use at first and most recent intercourse.[4]

❖ Teens in the U.S. are more likely to have sexual intercourse before the age of 15 and have shorter and more sporadic relationships than teens in other countries. As a result, they are more likely to have more than one partner in a given year.[4]

Contraception

❖ The majority of sexually active teens use contraceptives the first time they have sex. The most common method used is the condom (68% of teen girls and 80% of teen boys).[5]

❖ Parental notification is not required for teens to get birth control.[6]

❖ Teens in the U.S. and Europe have similar levels of sexual activity, but teens in Europe are more likely to use contraceptives and more effective ones. Therefore, they have much lower teen pregnancy rates.[7]

❖ Despite its decline, the US teen pregnancy rate continues to be the highest in the developed world.[8]

❖ Since 1968, the government has provided family planning funding (Title X);

the 2,500 federally funded family planning agencies operate 5,200 clinic sites; one of the most common providers is Planned Parenthood.[9]

❖ Emergency contraception sold as Plan B (also called "morning after," "aftersex" or "post-coital" birth control) can be used within 72 hours of unprotected intercourse to prevent pregnancy. It is available without a prescription for those 17 and older. Experts estimate that easy access to Plan B could reduce the number of abortions in the U.S. by half. In 2003, FDA's own panel of experts vote voted 23–4 in favor of over-the-counter status. Nonetheless, the FDA has refused to make it available to those under 17 without a prescription.[10]

Abortion

❖ Abortion was made legal in a few states in 1970 and throughout the country in 1973 by the Supreme Court. The *Roe v Wade* decision prohibits states from restricting abortion in the first trimester (available at her request) and allows states to regulate abortion to assure its safety in the second trimester and prohibit it, except to save the pregnant women's life or health in the third trimester.[11]

❖ In subsequent rulings, the Court has upheld the right to abortion, while giving states the right to legislate various kinds of restrictions. For example, state laws have been enacted that require notification of husbands or, in the case of minors, a parent; require a waiting period of up to 24 hours; and/or prohibit the use of public facilities for abortions.[12]

❖ Although most teens (61%) who have abortions do so with at least one parent's knowledge, 38 states (as of May 2013) have mandatory parental consent or notification laws in effect for a minor seeking an abortion.[13]

❖ One in three women will have an abortion, and abortion remains the most common surgical procedure for women in the U.S.[14]

❖ Access to abortion is a concern: 87% of all U.S. counties have no abortion provider.[14]

❖ RU-486/Mifepristone ("abortion pill" or medication abortion) was approved for marketing in 2000 as an alternative to surgical abortion. It must be taken within 63 days of pregnancy. It causes a woman to have her period; therefore, anything attached to the wall of her uterus will be expelled as if she is menstruating.[15]

Sex Education

❖ Only 23 states, including the District of Columbia, require schools to provide sexuality education. However, in many states these mandates or policies preclude teaching about such subjects as intercourse, abortion, masturbation, homosexuality, condoms and safer sex.[16]

❖ Thirty-three states, including the District of Columbia, require schools to provide STI, HIV, and/or AIDS education. However, some of these states require that education teach abstinence-only until marriage and not information on safer sex or condom use.[16]

❖ The vast majority of Americans support comprehensive sexuality education— medically accurate, age-appropriate education that includes information about both abstinence and contraception—and believe young people should be given information about how to protect themselves from unintended pregnancies and sexually transmitted diseases (STDs).[17]

❖ Since 1997 the federal government has invested more than $1.5 billion dollars in abstinence-only programs—proven ineffective programs which censor or exclude important information that could help young people protect their health. In 2010, a major shift in how the country approaches sexuality education.

The Obama administration provides $180 million in funding for more comprehensive approaches to sex education through the Teen Pregnancy Prevention Initiative, which provides grants to public and private entities for medically accurate and age-appropriate teen pregnancy prevention and positive youth development programs, and the Personal Responsibility Education Program, which provides young people with medically accurate and age-appropriate sex education in order to help them reduce their risk of unintended pregnancy, HIV/AIDS, and other STDs. There also still exists $50 million in mandatory funding for the Title V abstinence-only program.[18]

❖ Numerous studies and evaluations published in peer-reviewed literature have found that comprehensive sexuality education (covering a wide range of topics, including abstinence, contraception and condom use) is an effective strategy to help young people delay their involvement in sexual intercourse. Research has also concluded that these programs do not hasten the onset of sexual intercourse, do not increase the frequency of sexual intercourse, and do not increase the number of a partners sexually active teens have.[19]

❖ Officials at the National Institutes of Health, The Institute of Medicine, the U.S. Centers for Disease Control and Prevention, the White House Office on National AIDS Policy, and the Surgeon General's Office have all publicly supported sexuality education programs that included information about abstinence, contraception, and condom use. Prominent public health organizations also support comprehensive sexuality education including the American Medical Association, the American Academy of Pediatrics, the American College of Obstetrics and Gynecology, and the Society for Adolescent Medicine. In fact, more than 140 mainstream national organizations focusing on young people and health issues including Advocates for Youth, Girls Inc., the National Association for the Advancement of Colored People, and the YWCA of the USA have joined together as the National Coalition to Support Sexuality Education committed to assuring comprehensive sexuality education for all youth in United States.[20]

❖ In 2011, the Future of Sex Education published *National sexuality education standards: Core content and skills, K–12* to provide clear consistent guidance on minimum standards for sex education.[21]

HIV/AIDS

❖ An estimated 1.3 million people were living with HIV/AIDS in the United States by the end of 2007.[22]

❖ Out of a concern for the rising number of STIs, including HIV, as well as concern for other issues of unplanned pregnancy, abortion and sexual abuse, the Surgeon General issued a report in 2001 entitled, *Call to Action to Promote Sexual Health and Responsible Sexual Behavior.* The purpose of the report was to initiate a national dialogue on issues of sexuality, sexual health, and responsible sexual behavior.[23]

❖ Women account for an increasing proportion of people with HIV and AIDS, but men still account for the largest proportion.[22]

❖ After the introduction of antiretroviral therapy in 1995–1996, AIDS-related deaths fell steeply in the United States until the late 1990s and then continued to decline more gradually; the number of AIDS related deaths are 69% lower than in 1994.[22]

❖ The percentage of the United States' adult population that has been diagnosed with HIV or AIDS is six times greater than in Germany, three times greater than in the Netherlands, and one-and-a-half times greater than in France.[24]

LGBT issues

❖ The symbolic birth of the gay rights movement occurred in 1969 in New York city when police raided a gay bar, the Stonewall. Police raids on gay bars were common occurrences, but this time the bar's patrons resisted and fought back. A riot ensued and did not end until the following day. The Stonewall incident served as a catalyst for the formation of gay rights groups, and activities such as Gay Pride Week and parades are held in yearly commemoration of the Stonewall riot.[25]

❖ As of 2013, same-sex marriage is recognized in 14 states California, Connecticut, Delaware, Iowa, Maine, Maryland, Massachusetts (the first in 2003), Minnesota, New Hampshire, New Jersey, New York, Rhode Island, Vermont, Washington and the District of Columbia. Six states offer broad protections: Colorado, Hawaii, Illinois, Nevada, Oregon, and Wisconsin.[26]

❖ The Defense of Marriage Act (DOMA) was enacted in 1996, and allowed states to refuse to recognize same-sex marriages of other states. This was ruled unconstitutional in 2013.[27]

❖ By the end of the 20th Century, Sodomy laws were repealed or overturned in most American states, and those that still remained were ruled unconstitutional in the 2003 ruling in *Lawrence v. Texas.*[28]

❖ Starting in 2011, gay and lesbian individuals were allowed to serve openly in the military. Military policy and legislation previously prohibited gays and lesbians from serving, and later in 1993 passed legislation prohibiting gays and lesbians from serving openly (don't ask don't tell).[29]

Prostitution[30]

❖ Prostitution is illegal except in certain counties of Nevada where is it restricted to state-licensed brothels. Technically the laws regarding prostitution apply both to the seller of sex (the prostitute) and the purchaser of sex (the client, the john); however, it is more often the prostitute than the customer who is charged with a crime.

❖ Over a million people have worked as prostitutes in the United States.

❖ Several organizations are working for the rights of prostitutes including COYOTE (Call Off Your Old Tired Ethics), the U.S. Prostitutes Collective, and the National Task Force on Prostitution.

Pornography

❖ Pornography, sexually explicit material meant to be sexually arousing, has been subject to many laws throughout recent history. Since 1973, individual states have been allowed to develop their own legislation.[31]

❖ Pornography is an $8 billion dollar a year business. Half of all adult videos in the U.S. are bought or rented by women alone or women in couples.[32]

❖ Child pornography is against the law. In 1977, the U.S. passed the Protection of Children Against Sexual Exploitation Act. Since then, those involved in child pornography have been vigorously prosecuted. In 2003, the U.S. Supreme Court upheld a provision of the Children's Internet Protection Act that requires public libraries receiving federal funding to put anti-porn Internet filters on their computers or lose funding.[33]

Resources

▶ Advocates for Youth *http://www.advocatesforyouth.org*

▶ American Assoc. of Sex Educators, Counselors & Therapists *http://www.aasect.org*

▶ Planned Parenthood Federation of America *http://www.plannedparenthood.org*

▶ Sex Information and Education Council of the United States (SIECUS) *http://www.siecus.org*

▶ Society for the Scientific Study of Sexuality (SSSS) *http://www.sexscience.org/*

VIETNAM

Major Cities:	Ho Chi Minh, Hanoi, Hue, Danang
Ethnic Groups:	Kinh (Viet) 86%, Tay 2%, Thai 2%, Muong 2%, Khome 1%, Hoa 1%, Nun 1%, Hmong 1%
Languages:	Vietnamese (official), English (increasingly favored as a second language), some French, Chinese, and Khmer
Major Religions:	Buddhist 9%, Catholic 7%, Hoa Hao 2%, Cao Dai 1%
GDP per capita (PPP):	$3,600
Urban Population:	31%
Infant Mortality:	20 per 1,000 births
Life Expectancy:	Females: 75 years; Males: 70 years
Adult Literacy:	94%
Health Care System:	1 doctor per 1,000 people

References
- ❏ *Reference World Atlas* (2013). NY: DK Publishing.
- ❏ *The World Almanac and Book of Facts 2013* (2012). NY: World Almanac Education Group.
- ❏ *The World Factbook https://www.cia.gov/library/publications/the-world-factbook/.*

Sexual Activity[1]

❖ The legal age of consent is 18 years old.[1]
❖ Premarital sex appears to be rising. One study found 24–33% of unmarried men ages 21–24 had had oral, vaginal, or anal sex.[2]

Contraception

❖ Vietnam has had a two-child policy since the early 1990s. Concern about moving to a one-child policy (like China) centers around the cultural preference for a son, and therefore an increase in abortions would be expected if a one-child policy were to be adopted.[3]
❖ Approximately 75% of all married women use contraceptives. The IUD is the most popular method.[4]

Abortion

❖ Abortion is legal in Vietnam. With the government's two-child policy, it is expected (should the couple become pregnant a third time).[5]
❖ Vietnam has one of the highest abortion rates in the world.[5]
❖ There has been an increase in abortion among single women, suggesting an increase in premarital sex.[6]

Sex Education

❖ Faced with an increasing HIV-infection rate and an abortion rate thought to be among the highest in the world, Hanoi health officials opened the city's first sex education café in 1999. The café fills a void in sex education, as the subject is not taught in schools, and many parents admit they are too embarrassed to raise the issue with teenage children who are becoming increasingly sexually active.[7]

❖ Although Vietnam can be regarded as a fairly liberal society when it comes to sexual behavior, talking or writing about sexuality is a totally different matter.[7]
❖ A study published in 2011 found that most parents do not talk to their children about sex and ⅔ said they were uncomfortable talking to their children.[2]

HIV/AIDS[8]

❖ An estimated 250,000 people were living with HIV/AIDS at the end of 2011.

LGBT issues

❖ A year after the first gay pride parade, proposals and discussion occurred around same-sex marriage in 2012. Legislation was passed giving same-sex couples some rights.[9]
❖ Transgender rights lag behind and advocates are campaigning for rights.[10] Transgender people cannot get reassignment surgery (unless they are intersex) or change their gender on official documents.

Prostitution[11]

❖ Prostitution is illegal in Vietnam.
❖ Thousands of Vietnamese women and children are trafficked through the Vietnam-China border by illegal organizers who take them to Cambodia and from there to neighboring countries for prostitution purposes. Vietnamese pimps pretend to court village girls to bring them to the city, and then sell them to brothels.

Pornography[12]

❖ Illegal. Enforcement is strict. According to the legislatures, pornography harms Vietnamese standard values.

Resource

▶ Vietnam Family Planning Association (VINAFPA), 02 Le Duc Tho Street Mai Dich

Commune, Cau Giay District, Hanoi, Vietnam Tel: +84 (4) - 764 8091

ZIMBABWE

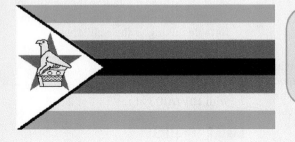

ZIMBABWE

POPULATION: 13,182,908

CAPITAL: **HARARE**

Major Cities:	Harara, Bulawayo, Chitungwiza
Ethnic Groups:	African 98% (Shona 2%, Ndebele 14%)
Languages:	English (official); Shona, Sindebele
Major Religions:	Syncretic (part Christian, part indigenous beliefs) 50%, Christian 25%, indigenous beliefs 24%
GDP per capita (PPP):	$600
Urban Population:	37%
Infant Mortality:	27 per 1,000 live births
Life Expectancy:	Females: 54 years, Males: 54 years
Adult Literacy:	91%
Health Care System:	< 1 doctor per 1,000 people; 71% of population has access to health services.

References
❑ *Reference World Atlas* (2013). NY: DK Publishing.
❑ *The World Almanac and Book of Facts 2013* (2012). NY: World Almanac Education Group.
❑ *The World Factbook* https://www.cia.gov/library/publications/the-world-factbook/

Sexual Activity

* The legal age for consent for sex is 12/16; it is illegal for same sex relations.[11]
* All oral and anal sex is prohibited.[1]
* The average age of first intercourse is 18.[2]

Contraception

* Condom availability is very inadequate and expensive; the equivalent of five condoms per adult per year are imported.[3]
* Although condom vending machines are accessible in clubs and bars, there are widespread taboos around the subject of sexuality, making it difficult for individuals to purchase the condoms.[4]
* Contraceptives are not readily available to women under the age of 18.[5]
* Early safety trials and focus-group discussions are underway in a number of countries, including Zimbabwe. Scientists have intensified their work to develop contraceptive technologies (such as vaginal microbicides) to prevent diseases such as HIV, especially those methods that are controlled by women.[5]

Abortion[5]

* Abortion is legal when:
  ◆ the woman has been raped or is a victim of incest.
  ◆ the fetus has genetic defects.
  ◆ it is to save the women's life or preserve physical health.

Sex Education[6]

* Due to the large number of HIV/AIDS cases, Zimbabwe has implemented many educational campaigns using multi-media and school-based programs to promote safer sex. Studies have confirmed the importance of sex education in the reduction of HIV infection.

HIV/AIDS

* An estimated 1.2 million people were living with HIV/AIDS in Zimbabwe at the end of 2011.[7]
* Zimbabwe has one of the highest AIDS prevalence rates in the world. HIV infection rates are highest before age 25, and among teenagers; women are especially vulnerable.[2]
* HIV prevalence in Zimbabwe has declined remarkably in recent years, dropping from 26 per cent to 14 per cent between 1997 and 2009. The most significant cause of the decline was seen to be the reduction in multiple sexual partnerships, with a 30% fall in men reporting extra-marital relationships. This can be partly attributed to the success of HIV prevention programs promoting fewer partners and condom use.[6]

LGBT issues

* In 2013, President Robert Mugabe attacked gay rights by describing LGBT people as "worse than pigs, goats and birds" and threatened to behead them.[8]
* The law recognizes three classes of "unnatural offenses": sodomy, bestiality, and a "residual group of proscribed 'unnatural' sexual acts referred to generally as 'an unnatural offense'" The absence of any definition of this third category enables any sexual act between men that falls short of sodomy to fall within it, provided there is a precedent, i.e. the act has previously been mentioned in court. These categories make no distinction between consensual and non-consensual acts, with the result that sentencing is inconsistent in lower courts, with consensual acts punished excessively, and non-consensual acts punished leniently.[9]

Prostitution[10]

❖ Prostitution is illegal, but thriving.

❖ In 2011, a senior government official proposed that prostitution be decriminalized in order to deal with corruption, HIV, and women's rights. She also proposed that the term "prostitute" be replaced by "pleasure engineer." Neither proposal was approved.

Pornography[11]

❖ Distributing/selling pornography is illegal, but it can easily be purchased on most street corners.

Resources

▶ Zimbabwe National Family Planning Council, P.O. Box 220, Southerton, Harare, Zimbabwe. Tel: 263/667656.

▶ United Nations Family Planning Association (UNFPA), Construction House, Fifth Floor, 110 Takawira St, P.O. Box 4775, Harare, Zimbabwe. Tel: 263-4-738793.

REFERENCES

AFGHANISTAN

1. Worldwide Ages of Consent. *http://www.avert.org/age-of-consent.htm.*
2. Afghanistan: Battle lines drawn over contraception. *http://www.rawa.org/temp/runews/2009/03/15/afghanistan-battle-lines-drawn-over-contraception.html*
3. UN Population Fund (UNFPA). *http://www.unfpa.org/emergencies/afghanistan/factsheet.htm*
4. Afghan Mullahs Promote Birth Control to Save Lives. *http://www.allvoices.com/contributed-news/5341996-afghan-mullahs-promoting-birth-control.*
5. Afghanistan: Penal Code. *http://cyber.law.harvard.edu/population/abortion/Afghanistan.abo.html.*
6. SANJUR: Afghan Women. *http://sanjar.blogspot.com/2008/07/afghan-women.html.*
7. HIV/AIDS in Afghanistan. *http://www.worldbank.org/en/news/feature/2012/07/10/hiv-aids-afghanistan.*
8. Statistics by Country for STDs. *http://www.cureresearch.com/s/stds/stats-country.htm.*
9. UNHCR's Eligibility Guidelines for Assessing the International Protection Needs of Afghan Asylum-Seekers. *http://www.unhcr.org/cgi-bin/texis/vtx/home.*
10. Afghanistan: Human Rights *http://www.ecoi.net/188769::afghanistan/314492.313155.7978...mr/sexual-orientation.htm.*
11. Despite denial and punishment, sex trade thrives in Afghanistan. *http://www.unifem.org/afghanistan/media/news/detail.php?storyID = 504.*
12. Boys in Afghanistan Sold Into Prostitution, Sexual Slavery. *http://www.digitaljournal.com/article/246409/Boys_in_Afghanistan_Sold_Into_Prostitution_Sexual_Slavery.*
13. Porn gains big following in Afghanistan. *http://www.sunnahonline.com/ilm/contemporary/post_taliban/0004.htm.*

AUSTRALIA

1. Legal Age of Consent. *http://www.ageofconsent.com/ageofconsent.htm*
2. Mazza, D et al. Current contraceptive management in Australian general practice: An analysis of BEACH data. Medical Journal of Australia, 2012 Available at: *https://www.mja.com.au/journal/2012/197/2/current-contraceptive-management-australian-general-practice-analysis-beach-data*
3. Reproductive rights around the world. Slate Magazine, May 30, 2013 *http://www.slate.com/articles/news_and_politics/map_of_the_week/2013/05/abortion_and_birth_control_a_global_map.html*
4. Condom sales in schools considered. *Facts on File.* 1992;52:336.
5. UNAIDS/WHO Epidemiological Fact Sheets by Country. *http://www.who.int/hiv/pub/epidemiology/facts/en/*
6. UNAIDS Fact Sheet: Oceania. *http://www.unaids.org/en/Regions_Countries/Regions/Oceania.asp.*

7. Dynes W, ed. *Encyclopedia of Homosexuality.* New York: Guilford; 1990.
8. Australia ends a prohibition on homosexuals in military, *The New York Times*, Nov. 24, 1992.
9. International Gay and Lesbian Human Rights Commission: Australia. *http://www.iglhrc.org/cgi-bin/iowa/region/122.html.*
10. Australian government guidelines on the recognition of sex and gender. (May 2013). *http://www.ag.gov.au/Publications/Pages/AustralianGovernmentGuidelinesonthe RecognitionofSexandGender.aspx*
11. State by State Laws in Australia. *http://www.scarletalliance.org.au/laws/*
12. Australia's Censorship System. *http://libertus.net/censor/auscensor.html*

AUSTRIA

1. Legal Age of Consent. *http://www.ageofconsent.com/ageofconsent.htm*
2. Bennett CL, Schwartz B, Marberger M. Health care in Austria: Universal access, national health insurance and private health. *JAMA.* 1993;269:2798–2804.
3. Rolston B, Eggert, A. *Abortion In the New Europe: A Comparative Handbook.* Westport, CT: Greenwood Press; 1994.
4. Traun-Vogt G, Kostenwein W. First love and heart beat in Austria. *Choices.* 1996;25:15.
5. Meredith P, Thomas L. *Planned Parenthood in Europe: A Human Rights Perspective.* Dover, NH: Croom Helm; 1986
6. Emergency contraception in Austria. *http://www.euromonitor.com/emergency-contraception-in-austria/report*
7. Austria—Harvard School of Public Health. *http://www.hsph.harvard.edu/population/abortion/Austria.abo.htm*
8. The Alan Guttmacher Institute. *Sharing Responsibility: Women, Society, and Abortion Worldwide.* New York: The Alan Guttmacher Institute; 1999.
9. FDA approves RU 486. *Choices.* 2000;28:32.
10. Sex Education in Europe: The Safe Project by IPPF. *http://www.sexarchive.info/BIB/SexEd/SexEd.html#3.1*
11. UNAIDS Epidemiological Fact Sheets by Country. *http://www.unaids.org/en/regionscountries/countries/austria/*
12. International Lesbian, Gay, Bisexual, Trans and Intersex Association: Austria. *http://www.ilga-europe.org/home/guide/country_by_country/austria/.*
13. Prostitution in Austria. *http://www.austria.gv.at/site/6852/default.aspx*
14. Francoeur, R. Austria: Pornography and Erotic. *The International Encyclopedia of Sexuality.* NY: Continuum; 2001. Available at: *http://www.sexarchive.info/IES/austria.html*

BELGIUM

1. Legal Age of Consent. *http://www.ageofconsent.com/ageofconsent.htm*
2. The Alan Guttmacher Institute. *Sharing Responsibility: Women, Society, and Abortion Worldwide.* New York: The Alan Guttmacher Institute; 1999.
3. Donnay F. Safe Abortions in an illegal context: Perceptions from service providers in Belgium. *Studies in Family Planning.* 1993;24:150–157.

4. UNICEF, *A League Table of Teenage Births in Rich Countries.* Florence, Italy: UNICEF Innocenti Centre; July 2002.

5. FDA approves RU 486. *Choices.* 2000;28:32.

6. Cherbonnier A. Belgium: A training programme in AIDS prevention. *Planned Parenthood in Europe.* 1990;19:17.

7. Sex Education in Europe: The Safe Project by IPPF. *http://www.sexarchive.info/BIB/SexEd/SexEd.html#3.1*

8. UNAIDS Epidemiological Fact Sheets by Country. *http://www.unaids.org/en/regionscountries/countries/belgium/*

9. International Lesbian, Gay, Bisexual, Trans and Intersex Association—Belgium. *http://www.ilga-europe.org/home/guide_europe/country_by_country/belgium*

10. Dynes W, ed. *Encyclopedia of Homosexuality.* New York: Guilford; 1990: 124–125.

11. Country report on human rights—Belgium. *http://www.state.gov/j/drl/rls/hrrpt/2007/100550.htm*

BRAZIL

1. Legal Age of Consent. *http://www.ageofconsent.com/ageofconsent.htm*

2. Hastings-Asatourian, B. Contraceptive education in Brazil. 2004. *http://www.academia.edu/168576/Contraception_Education_in_Brazil*

3. Moore, A. Gender role beliefs at sexual debut: Qualitative evidence from two Brazilian cities. *International Family Planning Perspectives.* 2006. *http://www.guttmacher.org/pubs/journals/3204506.html*

4. Center for Reproductive Rights. *Brazil: Women of the world—Laws and policies affecting their reproductive lives. http://reproductiverights.org.*

5. Center for Reproductive Rights. *Reproductive Rights 2000: Moving Forward. http://reproductiverights.org.*

6. Brazilian president signs law permitting abortion after papal visit. CAN, August 3, 2013. *http://www.catholicnewsagency.com/news/brazilian-president-signs-law-permitting-abortion-after-papal-visit/*

7. Abortions in Brazil, though illegal, are common. Time magazine, June 2, 2010. *http://www.time.com/time/world/article/0,8599,1993205,00.html*

8. Ulcer drug used for abortions in Brazil. *Contemporary Sexuality.* 1993;27:6.

9. Egypto AC, Pinto MC, Bock SD. Brazilian organization develops sexual guidance programs. *SIECUS Report.* 1996;24:16–17.

10. UNAIDS Epidemiological Fact Sheets by Country. *http://www.unaids.org/en/regionscountries/countries/brazil/*

11. International Gay and Lesbian Human Rights Commission: Brazil. *http://www.iglhrc.org/cgi-bin/iowa/region/91.html.*

12. Brazilian judicial council orders notaries to recognize same-sex marriages. CNN May 15, 2013. Available at: *http://edition.cnn.com/2013/05/15/world/americas/brazil-same-sex-marriage/index.html?eref=edition*

13. Otchet A. Should prostitution be legal? UNESCO Courier. 1998; 51:37–39.

14. 2009 Human Rights Report: Brazil. *http://www.state.gov/j/drl/rls/hrrpt/2009/wha/136103.htm*

15. Francoeur, R. Brazil: Pornography and Erotic. *The International Encyclopedia of Sexuality.* NY: Continuum; 2001. Available at: *http://www.sexarchive.info/IES/brazil.html#8*

BULGARIA

1. Legal Age of Consent. *http://www .ageofconsent.com/ageofconsent.htm*
2. Bulgaria—European Institute of Women's Health 2012 report. *eurohealth.ie/ wp-content/uploads/2012/08/eu-reports/ **bulgaria**.doc*
3. Chernev T, Hadjiev C, Stamenkova R. The cost of family planning and abortion in Bulgaria. *Planned Parenthood in Europe.* 1994;23:12–13.
4. Cherneve T, Ivanov S, Dikov I, Stamenkova R. Prospective study of contraception with Levonorgestrel. *Planned Parenthood in Europe.* 1995;24:25.
5. Sex Education in Europe: The Safe Project by IPPF. *http://www.sexarchive.info/ BIB/SexEd/SexEd.html#3.3*
6. UNAIDS Epidemiological Fact Sheets by Country. *http://www.unaids.org/en/ regionscountries/countries/bulgaria/*
7. International Lesbian, Gay, Bisexual, Trans and Intersex Association: Bulgaria. *http://www.ilga-europe.org/home/guide/ country_by_country/bulgaria.*
8. Bulgaria moves away from legalizing prostitution. NY Times October 5, 2007. *http://www.nytimes.com/2007/10/05/world/ europe/05iht-bulgaria.4.7773739.html ?pagewanted = all*
9. Pornography: Bulgaria. *http://en.wikipedia .org/wiki/Pornography.*

CANADA

1. Canada's age of consent raised by 2 years *http://www.cbc.ca/news/canada/story/ 2008/05/01/crime-bill.html*
2. Trends in sexual experience among Canadian teens. SexulityandU.ca 2008. *http://www.sexualityandu.ca/sexual -health/statistics1/statistics-on-sexual -intercourse-experience-among-canadian -teenagers*
3. Black, A. Yang, Q., Wen, S.W. et al. (2009). Contraceptive use among Canadian women of reproductive age: Results of a national survey. Journal of Obstetrics and Gynaecology Canada, July, 627-640. *http://www .sexualityandu.ca/professionals/pdfs/ National%20Contraception%20Survey.pdf*
4. International Planned Parenthood Federation News. *Canada Approves Emergency Contraceptive as Non-prescription Drug* (April 2005). *http://www/ippf.org.*
5. Access to abortion in Canada. National Abortion Federation. *http://www.prochoice .org/canada/access.html*
6. McKay, A. (2013). Trends in Canadian national and provincial/territorial teen pregnancy rates: 2001–2010. *Canadian Journal of Human Sexuality. http://www.sieccan.org/ pdf/TeenPregancy.pdf.*
7. Medical Abortion in Canada. *http://www.canadiansforchoice.ca/ medicalabortion.html*
8. SIECCAN. Available at: *http://www.sieccan.org/*
9. Parents support sexuality education in schools. *http://www.sexualityandu.ca/ teachers/making-the-case-for-school-based -sexual-health-education/parents-support -sexual-health-education-in-schools*
10. Canada on top in sex ed. *The Tyee* March 25, 2009. *http://thetyee.ca/Life/2009/ 03/25/SexEd/*
11. UNAIDS Epidemiological Fact Sheets by Country. *http://www.unaids.org/en/ regionscountries/countries/canada/*
12. 1 in 7 has genital herpes: StatsCan, *The Canadian Press.* April 17, 2013.

http://www.ctvnews.ca/health/one-in-7
-canadians-has-genital-herpes-statscan-study
-1.1241792

13. International Gay and Lesbian Human Rights campaign. International Global Summary of Registered Partnership, Domestic Partnership, and Marriage Laws (November 2003). http://www.iglhrc.org/content/international-global-summary-registered-partnership-domestic-partnership-and-marriage-laws

14. Fisher L. Armed and gay. MacLean's. May 24, 1993;106:14.

15. Equal Marriage for Same Sex Couples: Canada. http://www.samesexmarriage.ca/.

16. Canadian transgender rights bill suffers legislative setback. Straight.com July 5, 2013. Available at: http://www.straight.com/life/398311/canadian-transgender-rights-bill-suffers-legislative-setback

17. Supreme court grapples with prostitution laws, hears 'fear mongering' behind decriminalization foes. The Canadian Press, June 13, 2013. http://news.nationalpost.com/2013/06/13/supreme-court-grapples-with-prostitution-laws-hears-fear-mongering-behind-decriminalization-foes/

18. Lewin T. Canada says pornography harms women and can be barred, The New York Times. Feb. 28, 1992;141:B7.

19. The evolution of pornography law in Canada. http://www.parl.gc.ca/Content/LOP/researchpublications/843-e.htm

20. Petiti, J. Rights of the Child: Child pornography on the Internet. United Nations Economic and Social Council, December 24, 2004.

CHILE

1. Legal Age of Consent. http://www.ageofconsent.com/ageofconsent.htm

2. Chile's teen sexual health sparks storm. Women's enews. September 21, 2006. http://womensenews.org/story/reproductive-health/060921/chile-teens-sexual-health-sparks-storm#.Uf7-VlNQ2Mw

3. Center for Reproductive Rights. Women's Reproductive Rights in Chile: A Shadow Report. http://reproductiverights.org.

4. Chile: The struggle over emergency contraception. RH Reality Check, October 19, 2009. http://rhrealitycheck.org/article/2009/10/19/chile-the-struggle-over-emergency-contraception/

5. Conservative Chile will begin teaching sex education in schools. Latino Daily News. March 21, 2011. http://www.hispanicallyspeakingnews.com/latino-daily-news/details/conservative-chile-will-begin-teaching-sex-education-in-schools/6240/

6. UNAIDS Epidemiological Fact Sheets by Country. http://www.unaids.org/en/regionscountries/countries/chile/

7. Chilean paradoxes: LGBT rights in Latin America. IGLHRC August 13, 2012. http://iglhrc.wordpress.com/2012/08/13/chilean-paradoxes-lgbt-rights-in-latin-america/

8. More than 50,000 march in Chile for LGBT rights. NewNowNext. May 13, 2013. http://www.newnownext.com/more-than-50000-march-in-chile-for-lgbt-rights/05/2013/

9. Report on Human Right Practices 2006—Chile. http://www.state.gov/j/drl/rls/hrrpt/2006/78884.htm

10. UNFPA Global Population Policy Update: Chile. http://www.unfpa.org/public/cache/bypass/parliamentarians/pid/3615;jsessionid=F8E20729780244127A92682076D2954F?newsLId=7227

CHINA

1. Legal Age of Consent. *http://www.ageofconsent.com/ageofconsent.htm*
2. Problems of teenage pregnancies. China Daily. November 4, 2010. *http://www.china.org.cn/opinion/2010-11/04/content_21269885.htm*
3. Kelly G. *Sexuality Today 8th edition.* New York, NY: McGraw-Hill; 2006: 169.
4. Study shows that Chinese attitudes to sex and losing virginity have changed. China Daily Forum. March 17, 2013. *http://bbs.chinadaily.com.cn/thread-836954-1-1.html*
5. Burger, E (2013). Behind the red door: Sex in China. *http://www.richardmburger.com/books/behind-the-red-door-sex-in-china/excerpt/*
6. Contraceptive use in China. U.S.–China Today. March 30, 2012. *http://www.uschina.usc.edu/w_usci/showarticle.aspx?articleID = 18021&AspxAutoDetectCookieSupport = 1*
7. Center for Reproductive Rights. China. *http://reproductiverights.org.*
8. China sex ed: More than 90% of Chinese parents support increased sex ed in schools. The Huffington Post, June 6, 2013. *http://www.huffingtonpost.com/2013/06/06/china-sex-ed-over-90-perc_n_3396842.html*
9. UNAIDS Epidemiological Fact Sheets by Country. *http://www.unaids.org/en/regionscountries/countries/china/*
10. Chen, XS (2011). The epidemic of sexually transmitted infections in China: Implications for ocntrol and future perspectives. BMC Medicine. *http://www.biomedcentral.com/1741-7015/9/111*
11. International Lesbian, Gay, Bisexual, Trans and Intersex Association: China. *http://ilga.org/ilga/en/countries/CHINA/Law.*
12. In China, LGBT citizens seek assistance. *http://www.cnn.com/2013/06/27/world/asia/china-gay-lesbian-marriage*
13. 2008 Human Rights Report: China. *http://www.state.gov/j/drl/rls/hrrpt/2008/eap/119037.htm*
14. Gang C. China declares war on pornography. Beijing Review. March 19, 1990;33: 26–29.
15. They know it when they see it: Is all pornography banned in China? June 24, 2009. *http://www.slate.com/articles/news_and_politics/explainer/2009/06/they_know_it_when_they_see_it.html*
16. China shuts down over 60,000 porn websites. December 30, 2010. *http://www.reuters.com/article/2010/12/30/china-internet-idUSTOE6BT01T20101230*

COSTA RICA

1. Worldwide Ages of Consent. *http://www.avert.org/age-of-consent.htm.*
2. McCauley AP, Salter C. Growing numbers, diverse needs. *Population Reports.* 1995; 23:3–11.
3. The Alan Guttmacher Institute. Teenage sex occurs mostly outside marriage for men and within marriage for women around the world. *http://www.alanguttmacher.org/.*
4. Smith-Morris M. *The Economist Book of World Vital Statistics.* New York: Times Books; 1990.
5. IPPF Country Profiles: Costa Rica. *http://ippfnet.ippf.org/pub/IPPF_Regions/IPPF_CountryProfile.asp?ISOCode = CR.*
6. Pan American Health Organization. *Emergency contraception in the Americas.* Available at: *http://www.paho.org.*
7. Carroll JL, Wolpe PR. *Sexuality and Gender in Society.* New York: Harper Collins Publishers; 1996:452.
8. Victory against hedonistic sex "education" in Costa Rica. *http://www.vidahumana.org/english/hispanics/hispanics-costarica.html.*

9. UNAIDS/WHO Epidemiological Fact Sheets by Country. *http://www.unaids.org/en/regionscountries/countries/costarica/*
10. International Lesbian, Gay, Bisexual, Trans and Intersex Association: Costa Rica. *http://ilga.org/ilga/en/countries/COSTA%20RICA/Law.*
11. Costa Rica could be the first Central American country to allow gay civil unions. *http://qz.com/103649/costa-rica-could-be-the-first-central-american-country-to-allow-gay-civil-unions-by-accident/*
12. 100 countries and their prostitution policies: Costa Rica. *http://prostitution.procon.org/view.resource.php?resourceID=000772#costarica*

CUBA

1. Worldwide Ages of Consent. *http://www.avert.org/age-of-consent.htm.*
2. Not feminist, but not bad: Cuba's surprisingly pro-women health system. *http://nwhn.org/not-feminist-not-bad-cubas-surprisingly-pro-woman-health-system*
3. Legal abortion worldwide: Incidence and trends Sept 2007 *http://www.guttmacher.org/pubs/journals/3310607.html.*
4. The National Center for Sex Education, Cuba. *http://www.icpdtaskforce.org/about/Mariela-Castro-Espin.html*
5. Cuba embraces Dutch-style sex education. June 2011. *http://www.rnw.nl/english/bulletin/cuba-embraces-dutch-style-sex-education*
6. UNAIDS/ Epidemiological Fact Sheets by Country. *http://www.unaids.org/en/regionscountries/countries/cuba/*
7. A regime's tight grip—lessons from Cuba in AIDS Control. New York Times May 7, 2012. *http://www.nytimes.com/2012/05/08/health/a-regimes-tight-grip-lessons-from-cuba-in-aids-control.html?pagewanted=all&_r=0*
8. International Lesbian, Gay, Bisexual, Trans and Intersex Association: Cuba. *http://ilga.org/ilga/en/countries/CUBA/Law.*
9. 100 countries and their prostitution policies: Cuba *http://prostitution.procon.org/view.resource.php?resourceID=000772#cuba*

CZECH REPUBLIC

1. Worldwide Ages of Consent. *http://www.avert.org/age-of-consent.htm.*
2. Kastanlova V. Increasing sexually transmitted disease rates among prostitutes in the Czech Republic. *Journal of Community Health.* 1995;20:219–223.
3. Contraception and Abortion in the Czech Republic. *http://www.expats.cz/prague/article/health-medical/contraception-abortion/*
4. Emergency contraception in the Czech Republic. May 2013. *http://www.euromonitor.com/emergency-contraception-in-the-czech-republic/report*
5. Sexuality Education in Europe: Czech Republic. *http://www.sexarchive.info/BIB/SexEd/SexEd.html#3.5*
6. UNAIDS/Epidemiological Fact Sheets by Country. *http://www.unaids.org/en/regionscountries/countries/czechrepublic/*
7. International Lesbian, Gay, Bisexual, Trans and Intersex Association: Czech Republic. *http://ilga.org/ilga/en/countries/CZECH%20REPUBLIC/Articles.*

8. 100 countries and their prostitution policies: Czech Republic. *http://prostitution.procon .org/view.resource.php?resourceID = 000772 #czech*

9. Prague wants to legalize prostitution. The Prague Monitor, June 2013. *http://praguemonitor.com/2013/06/25/ prague-wants-legalise-prostitution*

10. Pornography and sex crimes in the Czech Republic. Archives of Sexual Behavior 2010. *http://www.hawaii.edu/PCSS/biblio/articles/ 2010to2014/2010-porn-in-czech-republic.html*

11. Czech Penthouse launched. *CTK National News Wire*, April 12, 1994.

DENMARK

1. Worldwide Ages of Consent. *http://www.avert.org/age-of-consent.htm.*

2. *Sexual Rights of Young Women.* Denmark: The Danish Family Planning Association and The Swedish Association for Sex Education; 1995.

3. Patterns of contraceptive use in five European countries. American Journal of Public Health, 2000. *http://www.ncbi.nlm .nih.gov/pmc/articles/PMC1447615/pdf/ 10983197.pdf.*

4. Emergency contraception in Denmark. *http://www.euromonitor.com/emergency -contraception-in-denmark/report*

5. Center for Reproductive Rights: Denmark. *http://reproductiverights.org/*

6. RU489/prostaglandin briefing. *http://www.spuc.org.uk/education/ abortion/ru486.*

7. Sex Education in Europe. *http://www.sexarchive.info/BIB/SexEd/ SexEd.html#3.6*

8. UNAIDS Epidemiological Fact Sheets by Country. Available at: *http://www.unaids.org/ en/regionscountries/countries/denmark/*

9. International Gay and Lesbian Human Rights campaign. Antidiscrimination Legislation (April 1999). Available at: *http://www.iglhrc.org/cgi-bin/iowa/region/ 171.html.*

10. International Lesbian, Gay, Bisexual, Trans and Intersex Association: Denmark. *http://ilga.org/ilga/en/countries/DENMARK/ Articles.*

11. 100 countries and their prostitution policies. *http://prostitution.procon.org/view.resource .php?resourceID = 000772#denmark*

12. Kimmel M. *Men confront pornography.* New York: Crown Publishers;1990:233, 244.

EGYPT

1. Worldwide Ages of Consent. *http://www.avert.org/age-of-consent.htm.*

2. FGM/C in Egypt: Prevalence rate and prospectus. UNFPA. *http://egypt.unfpa.org/ english/fgmStaticpages/0c3b708e-9c55-4b05 -994f-a437f89a81d9/Egypt_Prevalence_rate _and_Prospects.aspx*

3. Center for Reproductive Rights. *Implementing Adolescent Reproductive Rights Through the Convention on the Rights of the Child. http://reproductiverights.org.*

4. Trottier D, Potter L, Taylor B, Glover L. Reports: User characteristics and oral con- traceptive compliance in Egypt. *Studies in Family Planning.* 1994; 25:284–292.

5. As Egypt birthrate rises, population policy vanishes. New York Times, May 3, 2013. *http://www.nytimes.com/2013/05/03/world/ middleeast/as-egypt-birthrate-rises-population -policy-vanishes.html?pagewanted = all*

6. International Consortium for Emergency Contraception. *http://www.cecinfo.org/*

country-by-country-information/status
-availability-database/countries/egypt/

7. Abortions are illegal but common in Egypt. *http://womensenews.org/story/the-world/ 040412/abortions-are-illegal-and-common -egypt#.UiJLELyE5jg*

8. School's out for Egypt's sex education. The Guardian Oct 7, 2010. *http://www. theguardian.com/commentisfree/2010/oct/07/ egypt-sex-education*

9. UNAIDS Epidemiological Fact Sheets by Country. *http://www.unaids.org/en/ regionscountries/countries/egypt/*

10. International Lesbian, Gay, Bisexual, Trans and Intersex Association: Egypt. *http://ilga.org/ilga/en/countries/EGYPT/Law.*

11. 100 countries and their prostitution policies. *http://prostitution.procon.org/view.resource .php?resourceID = 000772#egypt*

12. Egypt bans porn sites. NBC News.com March 28, 2012. *http://www.nbcnews.com/ technology/egypt-bans-porn-websites-581228*

FINLAND

1. Worldwide Ages of Consent. *http://www.avert.org/age-of-consent.htm.*

2. Kosunen M, Rimpela M. Improving adolescent sexual health in Finland. *Choices.* 1996;25:18.

3. Emergency contraception among Finnish adolescents. British Medical Journal, 2007. http://www.biomedcentral.com/ 1471-2458/7/201

4. Abortion worldwide: A decade of uneven progress, Guttmacher Institute. *http://www.guttmacher.org/pubs/Abortion -Worldwide.pdf*

5. Statistical report: Finland has the lowest abortion rate in the Nordic countries. March 2013. *http://www.thl.fi/en_US/web/en/ news?id = 33143*

6. RU486/prostaglandin briefing. *http://www.spuc.org.uk/education/abortion/ ru486*

7. Sexuality education in Europe. *http://www.sexarchive.info/BIB/SexEd/ SexEd.html#3.8*

8. UNAIDS Epidemiological Fact Sheets by Country. *http://www.unaids.org/en/ regionscountries/countries/finland/*

9. Lottes IL. Sexual health policies in other industrialized countries: Are there lessons for the United States? Journal of Sex Research. 2002;39:79–83.

10. International Lesbian, Gay, Bisexual, Trans and Intersex Association: Finland. *http:// ilga.org/ilga/en/countries/FINLAND/Law.*

11. 100 countries and their prostitution policies. *http://prostitution.procon.org/view .resource.php?resourceID = 000772#finland*

12. Pornography: Finland. *http://en.wikipedia .org/wiki/Pornography_by_region#Finland*

FRANCE

1. Worldwide Ages of Consent. *http://www.avert.org/age-of-consent.htm.*

2. European approaches to adolescent sexual behavior and responsibility: A call to action. Advocates for Youth, 1999. *http://www.advocatesforyouth.org/storage/ advfy/documents/european.pdf*

3. France cuts condom prices. The New York Times. Dec. 5, 1993:14

4. UNICEF, *A League Table of Teenage Births in Rich Countries.* UNICEF Innocenti Centre, 2001. *http://www.unicef-irc.org/publications/ pdf/repcard3e.pdf*

5. Promoting contraceptive use and choice: France's approach to teen pregnancy and abortion. Guttmacher Institute, June 2000. *http://www.guttmacher.org/pubs/tgr/03/3/gr030303.html*

6. Center for Reproductive Rights. Abortion worldwide: Twelve years of reform. July 2007. *http://reproductiverights.org/sites/default/files/documents/pub_bp_abortionlaws10.pdf*

7. France: Reproductive health care now free. Center for Reproductive Rights. April 2013. *http://reproductiverights.org/en/feature/france-abortion-contraception-free*

8. FDA approves RU 486. *Choices*. 2000; 28:32.

9. Jones RK, Henshaw SK. Mifepristone for early medical abortion: Experiences in France, Great Britain and Sweden. *Perspectives on Sexual and Reproductive Health*. 2002. *http://www.guttmacher.org/pubs/journals/3415402.html*

10. Sexuality education in Europe: France. *http://www.sexarchive.info/BIB/SexEd/SexEd.html#3.9*

11. UNAIDS Epidemiological Fact Sheets by Country. *http://www.unaids.org/en/regionscountries/countries/france/*

12. French bishop supports the use of condoms to prevent AIDS, New York Times, Feb. 13, 1996. *http://www.nytimes.com/1996/02/13/world/french-bishop-supports-some-use-of-condoms-to-prevent-aids.html*

13. International Lesbian, Gay, Bisexual, Trans and Intersex Association: France. *http://ilga.org/ilga/en/countries/FRANCE/Articles*.

14. The freedom to marry internationally: France. *http://www.freedomtomarry.org/landscape/entry/c/international*

15. 100 countries and their prostitution policies: France. *http://prostitution.procon.org/view.resource.php?resourceID = 000772#france*

16. Pornography: France. *http://en.wikipedia.org/wiki/Pornography_by_region#France*

GERMANY

1. Worldwide Ages of Consent. *http://www.avert.org/age-of-consent.htm*.

2. European approaches to adolescent sexual behavior and responsibility: A call to action. Advocates for Youth, 1999. *http://www.advocatesforyouth.org/storage/advfy/documents/european.pdf*

3. Most European women use contraceptives. 2001. *http://www.prb.org/Publications/Articles/2001/MostEuropeanWomenUseContraceptives.aspx*

4. European consortium for emergency contraception: Germany. *http://www.ec-ec.org/emergency-contraception-in-europe/country-by-country-information-2/germany/#pub3*

5. German bishops ok emergency contraception in rape cases. Fox News Feb 21. 2013. *http://www.foxnews.com/world/2013/02/21/*german-bishops-ok-emergency-contraception-in-rape-cases/

6. Center for Reproductive Rights. The World's Abortion Laws: Recent Changes and Recommendations for Action. *http://reproductiverights.org/*

7. FDA approves RU 486. Choices. 2000;28:32.

8. Sexuality education in Europe: Germany. *http://www.sexarchive.info/BIB/SexEd/SexEd.html#3.10*

9. UNAIDS Epidemiological Fact Sheets by Country. *http://www.unaids.org/en/regionscountries/countries/germany/*

10. Dynes W, ed. Encyclopedia of Homosexuality. New York: Guilford; 1990.

11. International Lesbian, Gay, Bisexual, Trans and Intersex Association: Germany. *http://ilga.org/ilga/en/countries/GERMANY/Articles*.

12. Germany to become the first European state to allow "third gender" birth certificates. August 17. 2013. *http://rt.com/news/third-gender-birth-germany-592/*

13. Prostitution in Germany. *http://en.wikipedia.org/wiki/Prostitution_in_Germany*

14. Why Germany is 'Europe's biggest brothel.' The Guardian June 12, 2013. *http://www.theguardian.com/world/shortcuts/2013/jun/12/germany-now-europes-biggest-brothel*

15. Pornography: Germany. *http://en.wikipedia.org/wiki/Pornography_by_region#Germany*

14. Why Germany is 'Europe's biggest brothel.' The Guardian June 12, 2013. *http://www.theguardian.com/world/shortcuts/2013/jun/12/germany-now-europes-biggest-brothel*

15. Pornography: Germany. *http://en.wikipedia.org/wiki/Pornography_by_region#Germany*

GREECE

1. Worldwide Ages of Consent. *http://www.avert.org/age-of-consent.htm.*

2. UNICEF, *A League Table of Teenage Births in Rich Countries.* UNICEF Innocenti Centre, 2001. *http://www.unicef-irc.org/publications/pdf/repcard3e.pdf*

3. United Nations. *Abortion Policies: A Global Review.* United Nations, 1992. *http://www.un.org/esa/population/publications/abortion/*

4. Sexuality education in Europe: Greece. *http://www.sexarchive.info/BIB/SexEd/SexEd.html#3.11*

5. UNAIDS Epidemiological Fact Sheets by Country. Available at: *http://www.unaids.org/en/regionscountries/countries/greece/*

6. International Lesbian, Gay, Bisexual, Trans and Intersex Association: Greece. *http://ilga.org/ilga/en/countries/GREECE/Law.*

7. 100 countries and their prostitution policies: Greece. *http://prostitution.procon.org/view.resource.php?resourceID=000772#greece*

8. Pornography laws: Greece. *http://en.wikipedia.org/wiki/Pornography_by_region#Greece*

9. Kelly G. *Sexuality Today* 8th ed. New York: McGraw-Hill Publishing: 2006: 47.

HUNGARY

1. Worldwide Ages of Consent. *http://www.avert.org/age-of-consent.htm.*

2. UNFPA: Hungary. *www.unfpa.org/webdav/site/global/shared/CO.../Hungary_b4_9.30.doc*

3. Camp S. "Postinor: The unique method of emergency contraception developed in Hungary. *Planned Parenthood in Europe.* 1995;24: 23–24.

4. Abortion worldwide: Seventeen years of reform. Center for Reproductive Rights, October 2011. *http://reproductiverights.org/sites/crr.civicactions.net/files/documents/pub_bp_17_years.pdf*

5. Abortion under attack in Hungary. Center for Reproductive Rights, March 31, 2011. *http://reproductiverights.org/en/press-room/abortion-under-attack-in-hungary*

6. Sexuality education in Europe: Hungary. *http://www.sexarchive.info/BIB/SexEd/SexEd.html#3.12*

7. UNAIDS Epidemiological Fact Sheets by Country. *http://www.unaids.org/en/regionscountries/countries/hungary/*

8. International Gay and Lesbian Human Rights Campaign. Global summary of registered part-

nership, domestic partnership, and marriage laws. November 2003. *http://www.iglhrc.org/content/international-global-summary* *-registered-partnership-domestic-partnership-and-marriage-laws*

9. International Lesbian, Gay, Bisexual, Trans and Intersex Association: Hungary. *http://ilga.org/ilga/en/countries/HUNGARY/*

Law.

10. 100 countries and their prostitution policies: Hungary. *http://prostitution.procon.org/view.resource.php?resourceID = 000772#hungary*

11. Pornography: Hungary. *http://en.wikipedia.org/wiki/Pornography_in_Hungary.*

INDIA

1. Worldwide Ages of Consent. *http://www.avert.org/age-of-consent.htm.*

2. Sharma V, Sharma A. The letterbox approach: A model for sex education in an orthodox society. *Journal of Family Welfare.* 1995;41:31.

3. Visaria L, Jejeebhoy S, Merrick T. From family planning to reproductive health: Challenges facing India. *International Family Planning Perspectives.* 1999. *http://www.guttmacher.org/pubs/journals/25s4499.html*

4. Center for Reproductive Rights. India. *http://reproductiverights.org/pub_bo_wowlaw_india.html.*

5. Studies in Short: Indian researchers test reversible male sterilization. *Contemporary Sexuality.* 1995;29:4.

6. In India, banking on the morning after pill. Time. May 26, 2010. *http://content.time.com/time/world/article/0,8599,1991879,00.html*

7. *Center for Reproductive Rights. Reproductive Rights 2000: Moving Forward. http://www/ippf.org.*

8. Every two hours in India, a woman dies from an unsafe abortion. Time. July 19, 2013. *http://world.time.com/2013/07/19/world-population-focus-on-india-part-2-unsafe-abortions/*

9. Abortion law, policy, and services in India: A critical review. Hirve, S. 2004. Reproductive

Health Matters. *http://www.jstor.org/discover/10.2307/3776122?uid = 3739800&uid = 2129&uid = 2&uid = 70&uid = 4&uid = 3739256&sid = 21102603211933*

10. Sexuality and the law: Indian parliament bans mention of fetus's gender. *Contemporary Sexuality.* 1994;28:13,15.

11. Center for Reproductive Rights. *Promote access to the full range of abortion technologies: Removing barriers to medical abortion.* September 2005. *http://reproductiverights.org/sites/default/files/documents/pub_bp_tk_technologies1.pdf*

12. World population focus on India Part 1: Sex Education. Time July 10, 2013. *http://world.time.com/2013/07/10/world-population-focus-on-india-part-1-sex-education/*

13. UNAIDS Epidemiological Fact Sheets by Country. *http://www.unaids.org/en/regionscountries/countries/india/*

14. UNAIDS Fact Sheet: Asia. *http://www.unaids.org/en/Regions_Countries/Regions/Asia.asp.*

15. In India, HIV history repeats itself. Thought Leader. July 27, 2013. *http://www.thoughtleader.co.za/msf/2013/07/27/in-india-hiv-history-repeats-itself/*

16. International Lesbian, Gay, Bisexual, Trans and Intersex Association: India. *http://ilga.org/ilga/en/countries/INDIA/Articles.*

17. Politicians of the third gender: The "she-male" candidates of Pakistan. The Statesman. May 7, 2013. *http://www.newstatesman.com/world-affairs/2013/05/politicians-third-gender-shemale-candidates-pakistan*

18. 100 countries and their prostitution policies: India. *http://prostitution.procon.org/view.resource.php?resourceID = 000772#india*

19. Sachs A. The last commodity: Child prostitution in the developing world. *World Watch.* 1994;7:24–30.

20. Aziz C. A life of hell for the wife of a god. *The Guardian.* June 10, 1995: 25.

21. Child prostitution rampant in India: Girls serve 10 customers a day says UN study. Bhaksar News. June 9, 2013. *http://daily.bhaskar.com/article/WOR-unicef-study-found-child-prostitution-to-be-rampant-in-india-where-girls-are-bro-4286473-PHO.html?seq=1*

22. India considers banning pornography as reported sexual assaults arise. New York Times, April 22, 2013. *http://india.blogs.nytimes.com/2013/04/22/india-considers-banning-pornography-as-reported-sexual-assault-rises/*

IRAN

1. Worldwide Ages of Consent. *http://www.avert.org/age-of-consent.htm.*

2. Metz HC. Iran: *A country study.* Federal Research Division, Library of Congress; 1987: 111.

3. Iran Focus: News and Analysis. *http://www.iranfocus.com/en/iran-general-/sex-orgies-std-on-the-rise-in-iran-hard-line-daily-warns-03470.html*

4. Carrington T. Iran enacts family size rule. *The Wall Street Journal,* May 17, 1993:A13.

5. International Planned Parenthood *Federation News. 16-Year old Iranian Woman Hanged 'For Acts Incompatible With Chastity'* (September 2004). *http://www/ippf.org.*

6. United Nations. *Abortion Policies: A Global Review.* New York: United Nations; 1992:63–64.

7. International update: Iran expands birth control options. *Contemporary sexuality.* 1996;30:9.

8. Iran's birth rate plummeting at record pace: Success provides a model for other developing countries. *http://www.mnforsustain.org/iran_model_of_reducing_fertility.htm.*

9. Changing parameters for abortion in Iran. *http://www.issuesinmedicalethics.org/144ie130.html.*

10. Gajewski, K. A. Iran beats the United States—Worth Noting—Sex Education Services. *The Humanist,* July 1, 2002.

11. UNAIDS Epidemiological Fact Sheets by Country. *http://www.unaids.org/en/regionscountries/countries/islamicrepublicofiran/*

12. Sex and ayatollahs. *http://www.guardian.co.uk/commentisfree/2008/jun/10/iran.middleeast.*

13. MacKay J. Global sex: Sexuality and sexual practices around the world. *Sexual and Relationship Therapy.* 20001:16:71–82.

IRELAND

1. Worldwide Ages of Consent. *http://www.avert.org/age-of-consent.htm.*

2. FPA profile: Irish Family Planning Association. *Planned Parenthood in Europe.* 1994;23:35.

3. International Planned Parenthood Federation. Country Profile: Ireland. *http://www.ippf.org.*

4. Breakwell CM, Fife-Schaw CR. Sexual activities and preferences in a United Kingdom sample of 16–20 year olds. *Archives of Sexual Behavior.* 1992; 21:271–293.

5. European consortium for emergency contraception: Ireland. *http://www.ec-ec.org/emergency-contraception-in-europe/country-by-country-information-2/united-kingdom/*

6. Irish abortion bill becomes law. BBC News. July 30, 2013. *http://www.bbc.co.uk/news/world-europe-23507923*

7. International update: Irish court asked to rule on right to information on abortion. *Contemporary Sexuality.* 1995:29:11.

8. Center for Reproductive Rights. *"Women on Waves" helping to turn the tide on abortion restrictions. http://reproductiverights.org.*

9. Irish abortion bill becomes law. BBC News. July 30, 2013. *http://www.bbc.co.uk/news/world-europe-23507923*

10. Sexuality education in Europe: Ireland. *http://www.sexarchive.info/BIB/SexEd/SexEd.html#3.14*

11. UNAIDS Epidemiological Fact Sheets by Country. *http://www.unaids.org/en/regionscountries/countries/ireland/*

12. International Gay and Lesbian Human Rights campaign. Antidiscrimination Legislation. *http://www.iglhrc.org/cgi-bin/low/article/takeaction/resourcecenter/809.html.*

13. International Lesbian, Gay, Bisexual, Trans and Intersex Association: Ireland. *http://ilga.org/ilga/en/countries/IRELAND/Articles.*

14. IHRC welcomes withdrawal of appeal in transgender case. Irish Human Rights Commission. June 2008. *http://www.ihrc.ie/newsevents/press/2010/06/21/ihrc-welcomes-withdrawal-of-appeal-in-transgender/*

15. Bill to criminalize men who use prostitutes. The Irish Times. May 2, 2013. *http://www.irishtimes.com/news/crime-and-law/bill-to-criminalise-men-who-use-prostitutes-1.1379547*

16. Pornography—Ireland. *http://en.wikipedia.org/wiki/Censorship_in_the_Republic_of_Ireland#Pornography*

ISRAEL

1. Worldwide Ages of Consent. *http://www.avert.org/age-of-consent.htm.*

2. International Planned Parenthood Federation. Country Profile: Israel. *http://www.ippf.org.*

3. International Planned Parenthood Federation News. *Emergency Contraception Available Without Prescription in Israel* (March 2002). *http://www/ippf.org.*

4. United Nations Population Division: Israel. *www.un.org/esa/population/publications/abortion/doc/israel.doc*

5. FDA approves RU 486. *Choices.* 2000;28:32.

6. Cavaglion G. The institutionalization of knowledge in Israeli sex education programs: A historical review, 1948–1987. *Journal of Sex Education and Therapy.* 2002;25:286–293.

7. Sex education needed new survey says. The Jerusalem Post, January 15, 2007. *http://www.jpost.com/Israel/Sex-education-needed-new-survey-says*

8. UNAIDS Epidemiological Fact Sheets by Country. *http://www.unaids.org/en/regionscountries/countries/israel/*

9. International Gay and Lesbian Human Rights campaign. Antidiscrimination Legislation *http://www.iglhrc.org/cgi-bin/low/article/takeaction/resourcecenter/809.html.*

10. International Lesbian, Gay, Bisexual, Trans and Intersex Association: Israel. *http://ilga.org/ilga/en/countries/ISRAEL/Articles.*

11. Israel, despite the divided attitudes on LGBT rights, beats Arab countries by a mile. JNS.org News Service. July 1, 2013. *http://www.jns.org/latest-articles/2013/7/1/israel-despite-divided-attitudes-on-lgbt-rights-beats-arab-countries-by-a-mile*

12. 100 countries and their prostitution policies: Israel. *http://prostitution.procon.org/view.resource.php?resourceID=000772#israel*

13. Knesset to consider censoring our Internet's naughtier bits. Times of Israel. May 24, 2012. *http://www.timesofisrael.com/knesset-to-consider-pornography-censorship-law/*

ITALY

1. Worldwide Ages of Consent.
   http://www.avert.org/age-of-consent.htm.
2. Perez MD, Livi-Bacci M. Fertility in Italy
   and Spain: The lowest in the world. *Family
   Planning Perspectives.* 1992; 24:162–171.
3. Mixed messages from the Catholic Church
   on contraception. Latitude News.
   *http://www.latitudenews.com/story/
   mixed-messages-from-the-catholic-church-on
   -contraception/*
4. Spinelli A, Grandolfo ME. Induced abortion
   and contraception in Italy. *Planned
   Parenthood in Europe.* 1991; 20: 18–19.
5. United Nations—Population Division: Italy.
   *www.un.org/esa/population/publications/
   abortion/doc/italy.doc*
6. Sexuality education in Europe: Italy.
   *http://www.sexarchive.info/BIB/SexEd/
   SexEd.html#3.15*

7. International update: AIDS gang defiant.
   Contemporary Sexuality. 1995;29:7.
8. International Planned Parenthood
   Federation. Country Profile: Italy.
   http://www.ippf.org.
9. UNAIDS Epidemiological Fact Sheets by
   Country. *http://www.who.int/
   hiv/pub/epidemiology/pubfacts/en/.*
10. International Lesbian, Gay, Bisexual, Trans
    and Intersex Association: Italy.
    *http://www.ilga-europe.org/home/
    guide_europe/country_by_country/italy*
11. 100 countries and their prostitution policies:
    Italy. *http://prostitution.procon.org/
    view.resource.php?resourceID = 000772#italy*
12. Italy's supercharged street-walkers. The
    Economist. 1998;348:40.
13. Pornography—Italy *http://en.wikipedia.org/
    wiki/Pornography_in_Italy*

*http://www.ilga-europe.org/home/
guide_europe/country_by_country/italy*

11. 100 countries and their prostitution policies:
    Italy. *http://prostitution.procon.org/
    view.resource.php?resourceID = 000772#italy*
12. Italy's supercharged street-walkers. The
    Economist. 1998;348:40.
13. Pornography—Italy *http://en.wikipedia.org/
    wiki/Pornography_in_Italy*

JAMAICA

1. Worldwide Ages of Consent.
   http://www.avert.org/age-of-consent.htm.
2. Youth Reproductive and Sexual Health in
   Jamaica. *http://www.advocatesforyouth.org/
   index.php?option = com_content&task = view
   &id = 434&Itemid = 177.*
3. Prevalence and correlates of sexual risk
   behaviors among Jamaican adolescents.
   International Perspectives on Sexual
   and Reproductive Health. 2011.
   *http://www.guttmacher.org/pubs/journals/
   3700611.html*

4. Jamaican and Barbadian health care
   providers' knowledge, attitudes and behaviors regarding emergency contraceptive
   pills. International Family Planning
   Perspectives. December 2007.
   *http://www.guttmacher.org/pubs/journals/
   3316007.html*
5. Jamaica: Offenses Against person Act.
   *http://cyber.law.harvard.edu/population/
   abortion/Jamaica.Abo.htm.*
6. Sexual attitudes and behaviors among
   young adolescents in Jamaica. International
   Family Planning Perspectives.
   *http://www.guttmacher.org/pubs/journals/
   2507899.html.*
7. Youth reproductive and sexual health in
   Jamaica. Advocates for Youth. April 2006.
   *http://www.advocatesforyouth.org/
   publications/434#references*

8. UNAIDS Epidemiological Fact Sheets by Country. *http://www.unaids.org/en/regionscountries/countries/jamaica/*

9. Jamaica's AIDS epidemic. *http://worldfocus.org/blog/2009/09/22/jamaicas-aids-epidemic-by-the-numbers/7354*

10. *Jamaica HIV/AIDS Epidemic Update Jan–June 2006.* National HIV/STD Control Program, Ministry of Health, Kingston, Jamaica. *http://www.jamaica-nap.org/aids_d.html*

11. International Lesbian, Gay, Bisexual, Trans and Intersex Association: Jamaica. *http://ilga.org/ilga/en/countries/JAMAICA/Law.*

12. The most homophobic place on earth? Time. April 12, 2006. *http://content.time.com/time/world/article/0,8599,1182991,00.html*

13. 100 countries and their prostitution policies: Jamaica. *http://prostitution.procon.org/view.resource.php?resourceID = 000772#jamaica*

1. Worldwide Ages of Consent. *http://www.avert.org/age-of-consent.htm.*

2. International Planned Parenthood Federation News. *Japan Alarmed by Increase in Teenage Sex* (June 2005). *http://www/ippf.org.*

3. Kelly G. *Sexuality Today 8th edition.* New York: McGraw-Hill Publishers; 2006:11.

4. International Planned Parenthood Federation. Country Profile: Japan. *http://www.ippf.org.*

5. Abortion still key birth control. The Japan Times. October 20, 2009. *http://www.japantimes.co.jp/news/2009/10/20/reference/abortion-still-key-birth-control/#.UiPmwryE5jg*

6. Kitazawa K. Sexuality issues in Japan. *SIECUS Report.* 1994;22:7–11.

7. UNAIDS Epidemiological Fact Sheets by Country. *http://www.unaids.org/en/regionscountries/countries/japan/*

8. International Lesbian, Gay, Bisexual, Trans and Intersex Association: Japan. *http://ilga.org/ilga/en/countries/JAPAN/Law.*

9. 100 countries and their prostitution policies: Japan. *http://prostitution.procon.org/view.resource.php?resourceID = 000772#japan.*

10. Editorial: Governments crack down on the Internet. *Information Society Trends Issues.* December 2, 1996.

11. Kristof ND. In Japan, brutal comics for women. *The New York Times.* Nov. 5, 1995: E1.

12. MacKay J. Global sex: Sexuality and sexual practices around the world. *Sexual and Relationship Therapy.* 2001:16:71–82

KENYA

1. Worldwide Ages of Consent. *http://www.avert.org/age-of-consent.htm.*

2. Barker G, Rich S. Influences on adolescent sexuality in Nigeria and Kenya: Findings from recent focus-group discussions. *Studies in Family Planning.* 1992; 23:199–210.

3. Lorch D. Unsafe abortions become a big problem in Kenya. *The New York Times.* June 4, 1995;3(N).

4. Center for Reproductive Rights. Kenya. *http://reproductiverights.org.*

5. Incidence and complications of unsafe abortions in Kenya. August 2013. *http://www.guttmacher.org/pubs/abortion-in-Kenya.pdf*

6. UNAIDS Epidemiological Fact Sheets by Country. *http://www.unaids.org/en/regionscountries/countries/kenya/*

7. Pew global attitudes report. October 4, 2007. *http://pewglobal.org/files/pdf/258.pdf*
8. International Lesbian, Gay, Bisexual, Trans and Intersex Association: Kenya. *http://ilga.org/ilga/en/countries/KENYA/Law.*
9. 100 countries and their prostitution policies: Kenya. *http://prostitution.procon.org/view .resource.php?resourceID=000772#kenya*

10. Francoeur, R. Kenya: Pornography and Erotic. The International Encyclopedia of Sexuality. NY: Continuum; 2001. *http://www2.hu-berlin.de/sexology/ IES/kenya.html*

MEXICO

1. Worldwide Ages of Consent. *http://www.avert.org/age-of-consent.htm.*
2. McCauley AP, Salter C. Meeting the needs of young people. *Population Reports.* 1995; 41:3–11.
3. Center for Reproductive Rights. *Reproductive Rights 2000: Moving Forward. http://reproductiverights.org.*
4. Center for Reproductive Rights. *Women's Reproductive Rights in Mexico: A Shadow Report. http://reproductiverights.org.*
5. Ignoring evidence, Mexico states move to increase abortion restrictions. Guttmacher Institute. April 9, 2009. *http://www.guttmacher.org/media/ inthenews/2009/05/14/Mexico.html.*
6. Kelly G. *Sexuality Today, 8th edition.* New York: McGraw-Hill Publishers; 2006:169.

7. UNAIDS Epidemiological Fact Sheets by Country: Mexico *http://www.unaids.org/ en/regionscountries/countries/mexico/*
8. International Lesbian, Gay, Bisexual, Trans and Intersex Association: Mexico. *http://ilga.org/ilga/en/countries/MEXICO/ Articles.*
9. 100 countries and their prostitution policies: Mexico. *http://prostitution.procon.org/view .resource.php?resourceID=000772#mexico*
10. Pornography Laws: Mexico. *http://en.wikipedia.org/wiki/Pornography _in_Latin_America*
11. Mexico No. 2 producer of child porn, lawmakers say. Fox News. January 26, 2012. *http://en.wikipedia.org/wiki/Pornography _in_Latin_America*

MOROCCO

1. Worldwide Ages of Consent. *http://www.avert.org/age-of-consent.htm.*
2. Adolescent and Youth Reproductive Health in Morocco. *www.policyproject.com/ pubs/countryreports/ARH_Morocco.pdf.*
3. Morocco—Welcome to the United Nations. *www.un.org/esa/population/publications/ abortion/doc/morocco.doc.*

4. UNAIDS Epidemiological Fact Sheets by Country. *http://www.unaids.org/ en/regionscountries/countries/morocco/.*
5. Morocco: The Treatment of Homosexuals. *http://www.unhcr.org/refworld/ publisher,IRBC,,MAR,469cd6af0,0.html.*
6. Prostitution in Morocco. *http://en.wikipedia.org/wiki/Prostitution _in_Africa#Morocco*

NEPAL

1. Worldwide Ages of Consent. *http://www.avert.org/age-of-consent.htm.*
2. Family Planning Fact Sheet: Nepal. *www.searo.who.int/.../Family_Planning _Fact_Sheets_nepal.pdf.*
3. Medical abortion increasing safe abortion access in Nepal. *http://www.ipas.org/ Library/News/News_Items/Medical_abortion _increasing_safe_abortion_access_in _Nepal.aspx.*
4. Barriers and opportunities for improved school based HIV/AIDS education in Nepal. *http://gateway.nlm.nih.gov/ MeetingAbstracts/ma?f = 102250197.html.*
5. UNAIDS Epidemiological Fact Sheets by Country. *http://www.unaids.org/ en/regionscountries/countries/nepal/*
6. International Lesbian, Gay, Bisexual, Trans and Intersex Association: Nepal. *http://ilga.org/ilga/en/countries/NEPAL/Law.*
7. Nepal census recognizes third gender for the first time. UNDP. *http://www.undp.org/ content/undp/en/home/ourwork/hiv-aids/ successstories/Nepal_third_gender_census _recognition/*
8. Nepal: Facts on Trafficking and Prostitution. *http://www.uri.edu/artsci/wms/hughes/ nepal.htm.*
9. Technology is ripping open Nepal's traditionally closed society. *http://www.nepalitimes.com.np/issue/2008/ 08/01/Nation/15095.*

NETHERLANDS

1. Worldwide Ages of Consent. *http://www.avert.org/age-of-consent.htm.*
2. Sexual and reproductive health: The Netherlands in international perspective. *The Rugters Nisso Group. 2009. http://www.rutgerswpf.org/content/facts -and-figures*
3. Doppenberg H. Free pill in The Netherlands: For how much longer? *Planned Parenthood in Europe.* 1994;23:8–9.
4. UNICEF, *A League Table of Teenage Births in Rich Countries.* Florence, Italy: UNICEF Innocenti Centre; July 2002.
5. Ketting E. Is the Dutch abortion rate really that low? *Planned Parenthood in Europe,* 1994;23:29–32.
6. Rolston B, Eggert, A. *Abortion In the New Europe: A Comparative Handbook.* Westport, CT: Greenwood Press; 1994.
7. FDA approves RU 486. *Choices.* 2000;28:32.
8. Sexuality education in Europe: The Netherlands. *http://www.sexarchive.info/ BIB/SexEd/SexEd.html#3.19*
9. UNAIDS Epidemiological Fact Sheets by Country. *http://www.unaids.org/en/ regionscountries/countries/netherlands/*
10. International Gay and Lesbian Human Rights campaign. Antidiscrimination Legislation *http://www.iglhrc.org/ cgi-bin/low/article/takeaction/ resourcecenter/809.html.*
11. Lambda Legal. International Recognition of Same-Sex Partnerships (March 30, 2001). *http://www.lambdalegal.org/cgi-bin/ iowa/documents/records?/record = 432*
12. International Lesbian, Gay, Bisexual, Trans and Intersex Association: The Netherlands. *http://ilga.org/ilga/en/countries/ NETHERLANDS/Articles.*
13. Janssen R. Gays in Dutch army. *Europe.* 1993;325:37.
14. The rule of common sense. *The Economist.* 2002;363:12–14.
15. Pornography: Netherlands. *http://en.wikipedia.org/wiki/Pornography _by_region#Netherlands*

NEW ZEALAND

1. Worldwide Ages of Consent. *http://www.avert.org/age-of-consent.htm.*
2. United Nations. *Abortion Policies: A Global Review.* New York: United Nations; 1992.
3. McCauley AP, Salter C. Growing numbers, diverse needs. *Population Reports.* 1995; 41:3–11.
4. New Zealand gives way birth control to combat abortion. *Catholic World News.* May 2, 1996.
5. Jamison E. *World Population Profile.* U.S. Bureau of Census, Washington, D.C. 1994:A–42.
6. Center for Reproductive Rights. *Emergency Contraception: Contraception, Not Abortion. http://reproductiverights.org/pub_art _icpdec2.html.*
7. Jones RK, Henshaw SK. Mifepristone for early medical abortion: Experiences in France, Great Britain and Sweden. *Perspectives on Sexual and Reproductive Health.* 2002;34:154–161.
8. International Planned Parenthood Federation. Country Profile: New Zealand. *http://www.ippf.org.*
9. Rosser BR. Male homosexual behavior and the effects of AIDS education: A study of behavior and safer sex in New Zealand and Southern Australia. New York: Praeger; 1991.
10. UNAIDS Epidemiological Fact Sheets by Country. *http://www.unaids.org/en/ regionscountries/countries/newzealand/*
11. New Zealand bans discrimination. *The Dominion of Wellington,* NZ. July 29, 1993.
12. International Gay and Lesbian Human Rights campaign. Antidiscrimination Legislation *http://www.iglhrc.org/search/ node/new%20zealand*
13. International Lesbian, Gay, Bisexual, Trans and Intersex Association: New Zealand. *http://ilga.org/ilga/en/countries/NEW% 20ZEALAND/Articles.*
14. 100 countries and their prostitution policies: New Zealand. *http://prostitution.procon.org/ view.resource.php?resourceID=000772# newzealand*
15. Petiti, J. *Rights of the Child: Child pornography on the Internet.* United Nations Economic and Social Council, December 24, 2004.

NORWAY

1. Worldwide Ages of Consent. *http://www.avert.org/age-of-consent.htm.*
2. The Alan Guttmacher Institute. *Sharing Responsibility: Women, Society, and Abortion Worldwide.* New York: The Alan Guttmacher Institute; 1999.
3. International Planned Parenthood Federation. Country Profile: Norway. *http://www.ippf.org.*
4. More women using IUDs, implants Guttmacher study shows. Women's Health Policy Report. August 3, 2013 *http://go.nationalpartnership.org/site/ News2?page=NewsArticle&id=34824&news _iv_ctrl=0&abbr=daily4_*
5. Free contraception can cut abortion rate in half. Emax Health. March 14, 2013. *http://www.emaxhealth.com/1275/4/36034/ free-contraception-can-cut-abortion-rate -half.html*
6. European consortium for emergency contra -ception: Norway. *http://www.ec-ec.org/ emergency-contraception-in-europe/country -by-country-information-2/norway/*
7. Abortion clinics in Europe: Countries with easy access. *http://www.abortion-clinics .eu/abortion-europe/easy-access-foreign -women/*

8. Sexuality education in Europe: Norway. *http://www.sexarchive.info/BIB/SexEd/ SexEd.html#3.20*

9. UNAIDS Epidemiological Fact Sheets by Country. *http://www.unaids.org/en/ regionscountries/countries/norway/*

10. International Gay and Lesbian Human Rights campaign. Antidiscrimination Legislation *http://www.iglhrc.org/search/ node/norway*

11. The freedom to marry internationally: Norway. *http://www.freedomtomarry.org/ landscape/entry/c/international*

12. New Norway law bans buying sex. BBC News. January 1, 2009. *http://news.bbc.co.uk/2/hi/7806760.stm*

13. Pornography: Norway. *http://en.wikipedia.org/wiki/Pornography.*

14. Petiti, J. *Rights of the Child: Child pornography on the Internet.* United Nations Economic and Social Council, December 24, 2004.

POLAND

1. Worldwide Ages of Consent. *http://www.avert.org/age-of-consent.htm.*

2. The Alan Guttmacher Institute. *Sharing Responsibility: Women, Society, and Abortion Worldwide.* New York: The Alan Guttmacher Institute; 1999.

3. Rolston B, Eggert, A. *Abortion In the New Europe: A Comparative Handbook.* Westport, CT: Greenwood Press; 1994.

4. Most European women use contraceptives. PRB News. *http://www.prb.org/Publications/ Articles/2001/MostEuropeanWomenUse Contraceptives.aspx*

5. Center for Reproductive Rights. *Reproductive Rights 2000: Moving Forward.* *http://reproductiverights.org.*

6. Henshaw SK, Singh S, Haas T. Recent trends in abortion rates worldwide. *International Family Planning Perspectives.* 1999;25:44–48.

7. International Planned Parenthood Federation News. *High Levels of Illegal Abortion Found in Poland* (November 2005). *http://www/ippf.org.*

8. Sexuality education in Europe: Poland. *http://www.sexarchive.info/BIB/SexEd/ SexEd.html#3.21*

9. UNAIDS Epidemiological Fact Sheets by Country. *http://www.unaids.org/en/ regionscountries/countries/poland/*

10. International Lesbian, Gay, Bisexual, Trans and Intersex Association: Poland. *http://ilga.org/ilga/en/countries/POLAND/ Articles.*

11. 100 countries and their prostitution policies: Poland. *http://prostitution.procon.org/view .resource.php?resourceID = 000772#poland*

12. Pornography Laws: Poland. *http://en.wikipedia.org/wiki/Pornography _by_region#Poland*

PORTUGAL

1. Worldwide Ages of Consent. *http://www.avert.org/age-of-consent.htm.*

2. Portugal. International Women's Rights Action Watch. *http://www1.umn.edu/ humanrts/iwraw/publications/countries/ portugal.htm*

3. European consortium for emergency contra -ception: Portugal. *http://www.ec-ec.org/ emergency-contraception-in-europe/country -by-country-information-2/portugal/*

4. Center for Reproductive Rights. Reproductive Rights 2000: Moving Forward. *http://reproductiverights.org.*

5. Sexuality education in Europe: Portugal. *http://www.sexarchive.info/BIB/SexEd/ SexEd.html#3.22*
6. UNAIDS Epidemiological Fact Sheets by Country. *http://www.unaids.org/en/ regionscountries/countries/portugal/*
7. European HIV and AIDS statistics. Avert, 2011. *http://www.avert.org/hiv -aids-europe.htm*
8. International Lesbian, Gay, Bisexual, Trans and Intersex Association: Portugal.

http://www.ilga-europe.org/content/search? SearchText = portugal&SearchButton = Search
9. 100 countries and their prostitution policies. *http://prostitution.procon.org/view .resource.php?resourceID = 000772#portugal.*
10. Pornography Laws: Portugal. *http://en.wikipedia.org/wiki/Pornography _by_region#Portugal*

ROMANIA

1. Worldwide Ages of Consent. *http://www.avert.org/age-of-consent.htm.*
2. Johnson B, Horga M, Andronache L. Contraception and abortion in Romania. The Lancet. 1993;341:875–878.
3. UNICEF, *A League Table of Teenage Births in Rich Countries.* UNICEF Innocenti Centre, 2001. *http://www.unicef-irc.org/publications/ pdf/repcard3e.pdf*
4. Relationship between contraception and abortion: A review of the evidence. International Family Planning Perspectives, March 2003. *http://www.guttmacher.org/ pubs/journals/2900603.html*
5. The Alan Guttmacher Institute. *Sharing Responsibility: Women, Society, and Abortion Worldwide.* New York: The Alan Guttmacher Institute; 1999.

6. Sex education remains a black hole in Romania. The Balkan Insight. April 23, 2012. *http://www.balkaninsight.com/en/article/ most-romanian-women-not-interested-in -family-planning*
7. UNAIDS Epidemiological Fact Sheets by Country. *http://www.unaids.org/en/ regionscountries/countries/romania/*
8. International Lesbian, Gay, Bisexual, Trans and Intersex Association: Romania. *http://ilga .org/ilga/en/countries/ROMANIA/Law.*
9. 100 countries and their prostitution policies. *http://prostitution.procon.org/view.resource .php?resourceID = 000772#romania*
10. Pornography Laws: Romania. *http://en.wikipedia.org/wiki/Pornography _by_region#Romania*

RUSSIAN FEDERATION

1. Worldwide Ages of Consent. *http://www.avert.org/age-of-consent.htm.*
2. Trends in Family Planning in Russia, 1994 to 2003. Perspectives on Sexual and Reproductive Health, March 2009. *http://www.ncbi .nlm.nih.gov/pubmed/19291128*
3. UN Population Development. World Contraceptive Usage 2007.
4. Ellertson C. Expanding access to emergency contraception in developing countries. *Family Planning Perspectives.* 1995;26:251–263.

5. Popov A. A short history of abortion and population policy in Russia. *Planned Parenthood in Europe.* 1993;22;23–25.
6. Center for Reproductive Rights. *Abortion and the Law: Ten Years of Reform. http://reproductiverights.org/wn _abortion.html.*
7. The Alan Guttmacher Institute. *Sharing Responsibility: Women, Society, and Abortion Worldwide.* New York: The Alan Guttmacher Institute; 1999.

8. FDA approves RU 486. *Choices.* 2000;28:32.
9. Zhuravleva IV. The health behavior of adolescents and sexually transmitted disease. *Russian Education & Society.* 2001;43:72–92.
10. UNAIDS Epidemiological Fact Sheets by Country. *http://www.unaids.org/en/regionscountries/countries/russianfederation/*
11. Russia: Death by indifference. Pulitzer Center, July 2, 2013. *http://pulitzercenter.org/reporting/russia-st-petersburg-addict-treatment-recovery-public-health-drug-user-heroin-opiate-methadone-society-HIV-AIDS*
12. International Lesbian, Gay, Bisexual, Trans and Intersex Association: Russian Federation. *http://ilga.org/ilga/en/countries/RUSSIAN%20FEDERATION/Articles.*
13. Gay parades banned in Moscow for 100 years. BBC News. August 17, 2012. *http://www.bbc.co.uk/news/world-europe-19293465*
14. Russia OKs bill banning gay 'propaganda.' USA Today June 11, 2013. *http://www.usatoday.com/story/news/world/2013/06/11/russian-gay/2411939/*
15. How Russia's anti-gay law could affect the 2014 Olympics. Mother Jones, August 16, 2013. *http://www.motherjones.com/politics/2013/08/sochi-olympics-putin-anti-gay-law-explained*
16. Quigley J. The dilemma of prostitution law reform. *American Criminal Law Review.* 1992;29:1192–1234.
17. Goscilo H. New members and organs: Politics of porn. Genders. 1995;22:164.
18. Holman R. Moscow restricts pornography. *The Wall Street Journal.* June 6, 1994:A9.

RWANDA

1. Worldwide Ages of Consent. *http://www.avert.org/age-of-consent.htm.*
2. Family Planning in Rwanda. *http://www.intrahealth.org/files/media/5/fp_in_Rwanda.pdf.*
3. Rwanda Abortion Policy: Welcome to the UN. *http://www.un.org/esa/population/publications/abortion/doc/rwanda.doc.*
4. Rwandan Officials Promote Condom Use. *http://www.rhrealitycheck.org/blog/2009/07/01/rwandan-officials-promote-condom-use.*
5. UNAIDS Epidemiological Fact Sheets by Country. *http://www.unaids.org/en/regionscountries/countries/rwanda/*
6. On World AIDS Day: Rape, HIV and Lingering Genocide in Rwanda. *http://humanrights.change.org/blog/view/on_world_aids_day_rape_hiv_and_lingering_genocide_in_rwanda.*
7. International Lesbian, Gay. Bisexual, Trans and Intersex Association: Rwanda. *http://ilga.org/ilga/en/countries/RWANDA/Articles.*
8. Sisters of Rwanda. *http://www.theeye.co.rw/sisters_of_rwanda.php.*

SINGAPORE

1. Worldwide Ages of Consent. *http://www.avert.org/age-of-consent.htm.*
2. David JM. Don't count on me, Singapore. National Review. May 16, 1994.
3. Chua J. Un-studly. *The New Republic.* January 27, 1992:11–12.
4. International Planned Parenthood Federation. Country Profile: Singapore. *http://www.ippf.org.*
5. Chaun K. *Changing contraceptive choices of Singapore women. http://www.singstat.gov.sg.*

6. Sachdev P, ed. *International Handbook on Abortion*. New York: Greenwood Press; 1988:402–412.
7. International Planned Parenthood Federation. IPPF News: *Singapore to launch sex education programmes next year* (November 2000). *http://ippfnet.ippf.org/*.
8. UNAIDS Epidemiological Fact Sheets by Country. *http://www.unaids.org/en/regionscountries/countries/singapore/*
9. International Lesbian, Gay, Bisexual, Trans and Intersex Association: Singapore. *http://ilga.org/ilga/en/countries/SINGAPORE/Articles*.
10. 100 countries and their prostitution policies: Singapore. *http://prostitution.procon.org/view.resource.php?resourceID = 000772#singapore*
11. What is the law on pornography in Singapore. *http://singaporelegaladvice.com/what-is-the-law-on-pornography-in-singapore/*

SLOVAKIA

1. Worldwide Ages of Consent. *http://www.avert.org/age-of-consent.htm*.
2. Calculated injustice: The Slovak Republic's failure to ensure access to contraceptives. The Center for Reproductive Center, 2011. *http://reproductiverights.org/sites/crr.civicactions.net/files/documents/calculatedinjustice_2011.pdf*
3. Chudikova A. Reproductive health challenges in the Slovak Republic. *Planned Parenthood in Europe*. 1993;22:27.
4. Camp S. Postinor: The unique method of emergency contraception developed in Hungary. *Planned Parenthood in Europe*. 1995;24:23–24.
5. *Abortion laws in Europe*. National Abortion Campaign. London, England; 1995.
6. Sexuality education in Europe: Slovakia. *http://www.sexarchive.info/BIB/SexEd/SexEd.html#3.23*
7. UNAIDS Epidemiological Fact Sheets by Country. *http://www.unaids.org/en/regionscountries/countries/slovakia/*
8. International Lesbian, Gay, Bisexual, Trans and Intersex Association: Slovakia. *http://ilga.org/ilga/en/countries/SLOVAKIA/Articles*
9. 100 countries and their prostitution policies: Slovakia. *http://prostitution.procon.org/view.resource.php?resourceID = 000772#slovakia*
10. Slovakia's post-Communist porn industry. Radio Prague. May 6, 2005. *http://www.radio.cz/en/section/ice_special/slovakias-post-communist-porn-industry*

SOUTH AFRICA

1. Worldwide Ages of Consent. *http://www.avert.org/age-of-consent.htm*.
2. Lucas D. Fertility and family planning in southern and central Africa. *Studies in Family Planning*. 1992;23:31–39.
3. HIV risk perceptions and first intercourse among youth in Cape Town South Africa. International Family Planning Perspectives, September 2007, *http://www.guttmacher.org/pubs/journals/3309807.html*.
4. Dan O. Population studies in South Africa. *Studies in Family Planning*. 1993;24:
5. Emergency contraception is little known and rarely used by South Africans. International Family Planning Perspectives, June 2002. *http://www.guttmacher.org/pubs/journals/2812802.html*
6. Center for Reproductive Rights. *Reproductive Rights 2000: Moving Forward*. *http://reproductiverights.org*.

7. The Alan Guttmacher Institute. *Sharing Responsibility: Women, Society, and Abortion Worldwide.* New York: The Alan Guttmacher Institute; 1999.

8. FDA approves RU 486. Choices. 2000;28:32.

9. Sexuality and HIV/AIDS education in South African secondary schools. Open Society Initiative. October 25, 2012. *http://www.osisa .org/buwa/south-africa/sexual-and-hivaids -education-south-african-secondary-schools*

10. UNAIDS Fact Sheet: Sub-Saharan Africa. *http://www.unaids.org/en/Regions_Countries/ Regions/SubSaharanAfrica.asp.*

11. UNAIDS Epidemiological Fact Sheets by Country. *http://www.unaids.org/en/ regionscountries/countries/southafrica/*

12. International Gay and Lesbian Human Rights campaign. Antidiscrimination Legislation (April 1999). *http://www.iglhrc .org/cgi-bin/low/article/takeaction/ resourcecenter/809.html.*

13. International Lesbian, Gay, Bisexual, Trans and Intersex Association: South Africa. *http://ilga.org/ilga/en/countries/ SOUTH%20AFRICA/Articles.*

14. 100 countries and their prostitution policies. *http://prostitution.procon.org/view.resource .php?resourceID = 000772#southafrica.*

15. Pornography Laws: South Africa. *http://en.wikipedia.org/wiki/Pornography _by_region#South_Africa*

SPAIN

1. Worldwide Ages of Consent. *http://www.avert.org/age-of-consent.htm.*

2. Nieto E, DeCiria L. FPA youth programme in Spain. *Choices.* 1996;25:5–7.

3. Perez M, Livi-Bacci M. Fertility in Italy and Spain: The lowest in the world. *Family Planning Perspectives.* 1992;24:162–171.

4. Perez R. Emergency contraception at a youth service centre. *Planned Parenthood in Europe.* 1995;24:11–12.

5. Spain expands legal access to abortion. March 3, 2010. Guttmacher Institute. *http://www.guttmacher.org/media/inthenews/ print/2010/03/03/index.html*

6. FDA approves RU 486. Choices. 2000;28:32.

7. Sexuality education in Europe: Spain. *http://www.sexarchive.info/BIB/SexEd/ SexEd.html#3.24*

8. UNAIDSEpidemiological Fact Sheets by Country. *http://www.who.int/hiv/pub/ epidemiology/pubfacts/en/.*

9. New HIV vaccine developed in Spain. CRI English, March 29, 2013. *http://english .cri.cn/7146/2013/03/29/2361s756671.htm*

10. International Gay and Lesbian Human Rights campaign. Antidiscrimination Legislation Update. *http://www.iglhrc.org/ cgi-bin/low/article/takeaction/resourcecenter/ 809.html*

11. International Lesbian, Gay, Bisexual, Trans and Intersex Association: Spain. *http://ilga.org/ilga/en/countries/SPAIN/ Articles.*

12. Freedom to Marry: Spain. *http://www.freedomtomarry.org/landscape/ entry/c/international*

13. 100 countries and their prostitution policies: Spain. *http://www.freedomtomarry.org/ landscape/entry/c/international*

14. Pornography Laws: Spain. *http://en.wikipedia .org/wiki/Pornography_by_region#Spain*

SWEDEN

1. Worldwide Ages of Consent. *http://www.avert.org/age-of-consent.htm.*
2. The Danish Family Planning Association and Swedish Association for Sex Education. *The Sexual Rights of Young Women in Denmark and Sweden.* Denmark: Clausen Offset; 1995.
3. Lewin B, ed. *Sex in Sweden: On the Swedish Sexual Life.* Stockholm, Sweden: The National Institute of Public Health; 2000. *http://www.rfsu.se/en/Engelska/About-rfsu/ Resources/Statistics--Facts--Sweden-/*
4. Snyder P. *European Women's Almanac.* New York: Columbia Univ. Press: 1992;330–332.
5. Persson E, Gustafsson B, van Rooijen M. Subsidizing contraception for young people in Sweden. *Planned Parenthood in Europe.* 1994;23:2–4.
6. Rogala C, Anzen B. Late start for emergency contraception in Sweden. *Planned Parenthood in Europe.* 1995;24:15–17.
7. FDA approves RU 486. Choices. 2000;28:32.
8. Jones RK, Henshaw SK. Mifepristone for early medical abortion: Experiences in France, Great Britain and Sweden. *Perspectives on Sexual and Reproductive Health.* 2002;34:154–161.
9. Sexuality Education in Europe: Sweden. *http://www.sexarchive.info/BIB/SexEd/SexEd .html#3.25*
10. Lottes, IL. Sexual health policies in other industrialized countries: Are there lessons for the United States? *Journal of Sex Research.* 2002;39:79–83.
11. UNAIDS Epidemiological Fact Sheets by Country. *http://www.unaids.org/en/ regionscountries/countries/sweden/*
12. Your rights in Sweden. RFSL. *http://www.rfsl .se/?p = 3300*
13. Freedom to Marry. *http://www.freedomto marry.org/landscape/entry/c/international*
14. Gender-neutral 'hen' makes its legal debut. The Local, Dec. 12, 2012. *http://www.thelocal .se/45070/20121214/*
15. 100 countries and their prostitution policies: Sweden. *http://prostitution.procon.org/view .resource.php?resourceID = 000772#sweden*
16. Pornography—Sweden. *http://en.wikipedia .org/wiki/Pornography_by_region#Sweden*

SWITZERLAND

1. Worldwide Ages of Consent. *http://www.avert.org/age-of-consent.htm.*
2. The Alan Guttmacher Institute. *Sharing Responsibility: Women, Society, and Abortion Worldwide.* New York: The Alan Guttmacher Institute; 1999.
3. First sexual intercourse and contraception: A cross-national survey on the sexuality of 16–20 year olds in Switzerland. Swiss Medical World (2000). *http://www.smw.ch/ docs/pdf/2000_40/2000-40-041.PDF.*
4. Rolston B, Eggert, A. *Abortion In the New Europe: A Comparative Handbook.* Westport, CT: Greenwood Press; 1994:262–263.
5. Extra small condoms for 12 year-old boys go on sale in Switzerland. *http://www.telegraph.co.uk/health/ healthnews/7361181/Extra-small-condoms -for-12-year-old-boys-go-on-sale-in -Switzerland.html*
6. Center for Reproductive Rights. Abortion worldwide: Twelve years of reform. July 2007 *http://reproductiverights.org/sites/default/ files/documents/pub_bp_abortionlaws10.pdf*
7. FDA approves RU 486. *Choices.* 2000;28:32.
8. "Sex box" to get new as parents revolt. The Local, August 15, 2011. *http://www.thelocal .ch/20110815/847*

9. UNAIDS Epidemiological Fact Sheets by Country. *http://www.unaids.org/en/ regionscountries/countries/Switzerland/*
10. International Lesbian, Gay, Bisexual, Trans and Intersex Association: Switzerland. *http://ilga.org/ilga/en/countries/ SWITZERLAND/Articles.*
11. Rainbow families: Gays granted more adoption rights. SwissInfo.ch December 13, 2012. *http://www.swissinfo.ch/eng/swiss _news/Gays_granted_more_adoption_rights .html?cid = 34183066*
12. Switzerland: Zurich launches "sex drive-ins" CNN.com August 26, 2013. *http://www.cnn.com/2013/08/26/world/ Switze/Switzerland-sex-drive-ins/index.html*
13. Pornography in Switzerland. Swiss Criminal Code. *http://www.admin.ch/ch/e/rs/311_0/ a197.html*

THAILAND

1. Worldwide Ages of Consent. *http://www.avert.org/age-of-consent.htm.*
2. Kilmarx, A.L. et al. (2006) Sexual initiation, substance use, and sexual behavior and knowledge among vocational students in northern Thailand. *International Family Planning Perspectives,* 32(3). *http://www .guttmacher.org/pubs/journals/3212606.html*
3. UNFPA, Reproductive health of women in Thailand: Progress and challenges. July 11, 2005. *http://www.unfpa.org/upload/lib_pub _file/451_filename_rhwomenthailand.pdf*
4. Godley J. Kinship networks and contraceptive choice in Nang Rong, Thailand. *International Family Planning Perspectives.* 2001;27:4–10.
5. Ratanajamit,C. & Chongsuvivatwong, V. (2001). Survey of knowledge and practice on oral contraceptive and emergency contraceptive pills of drugstore personnel in Hat Yai, Thailand, *Pharmaco-epidemiology and Drug Safety,* 10(2):149–156.
6. UNFPA Maternal and neonatal health in East and Southeast Asia. March 2006. *http://www.unfpa.org/upload/lib_pub_file/ 613_filename_bkmaternal.pdf*
7. UNAIDS Epidemiological Fact Sheets by Country. *http://www.unaids.org/en/ regionscountries/countries/thailand/*
8. Phoolcharoen W. HIV/AIDS prevention in Thailand: Success and challenges. *Science.* 1998; 280:1873–1874.
9. International Lesbian, Gay, Bisexual, Trans and Intersex Association: Thailand. *http://ilga.org/ilga/en/countries/THAILAND/ Articles.*
10. Thailand, conservative but tolerant, may legalize gay marriage. Reuters. August 21, 2013. *http://uk.reuters.com/article/2013/ 08/21/uk-thailand-gay-marriage -idUKBRE97K04X20130821*
11. Jackson, P. (2003). Performative genders, perverse desires: A bio-history of Thailand's same-sex and transgender cultures. Intersections; Gender, history, and culture in the Asian context. *http://intersections .anu.edu.au/issue9/jackson.html*
12. 100 countries and their prostitution policies: Thailand. *http://prostitution.procon.org/ view.resource.php?resourceID = 000772 #thailand*
13. Seabrook J. Sex for sale, cheap thrills. *New Statesman & Society.* May 31, 1991:12–13.
14. Shetry A, Lee M, Vatiklotis M. Sex trade: For lust of money. *Far Eastern Economic Review.* December 14, 1995:22–23.
15. Pornography laws: Thailand. *http://en .wikipedia.org/wiki/Pornography_by_region #Thailand*

TURKEY

1. Worldwide Ages of Consent. *http://www.avert.org/age-of-consent.htm.*
2. International update: Turkey to revise school virginity tests. *Contemporary Sexuality.* 1995;29:9.
3. UNDP The dynamics of honor killings in Turkey. 2005. *http://www.unfpa.org/upload/lib_pub_file/676_filename_honourkillings.pdf*
4. Senlet P, Cagatay L, Ergin J, Mathis J. Bridging the gap: Integrating family planning with abortion services in Turkey. *International Family Planning Perspectives.* 2001;27:90–96.
5. Center for Reproductive Rights: Turkey. *http://reproductiverights.org/*
6. The Alan Guttmacher Institute. *Sharing Responsibility: Women, Society, and Abortion Worldwide.* New York: The Alan Guttmacher Institute; 1999.
7. News items: Sex education in Turkey. *Choices.* 1996;25:39.
8. International Planned Parenthood Federation. Country Profile: Turkey. *http://www.ippf.org.*
9. Turkey: Sex education remains taboo topic. Eurasianet.org. September 7, 2012. *http://www.eurasianet.org/node/65884*
10. UNAIDS Epidemiological Fact Sheets by Country. *http://www.unaids.org/en/regionscountries/countries/turkey/*
11. Turkey: Feminists, lesbians organize. *off our backs.* February 1996:7.
12. Protestors squelched, gay rights march brings many in Turkey back to the streets. New York Times. June 30, 2013. *http://www.nytimes.com/2013/07/01/world/europe/protests-squelched-gay-rights-march-brings-many-in-turkey-back-to-the-streets.html*
13. Turkey to become second majority Muslim nation to protect sexual minorities from discrimination. Gay Star News. August 15, 2013. *http://www.gaystarnews.com/article/turkey-become-second-muslim-nation-protect-sexual-minorities-discrimination150813*
14. 100 countries and their prostitution policies: Turkey. *http://prostitution.procon.org/view.resource.php?resourceID=000772#turkey*
15. Pornography laws in Turkey. *http://en.wikipedia.org/wiki/Pornography_in_Turkey*

UNITED KINGDOM

1. Worldwide Ages of Consent. *http://www.avert.org/age-of-consent.htm.*
2. Teenagers: Sexual health and behavior factsheet. FPA, January 2001. *http://www.fpa.org.uk/factsheets/teenagers-sexual-health-behaviour*
3. Teenage pregnancy factsheet. FPA, August 2010. *http://www.fpa.org.uk/factsheets/teenage-pregnancy*
4. Ingham R. *Exploring interactional competence: Comparative data from the UK and The Netherlands on young people's sexual development.* Paper presented at the International Academy of Sex Research; 1998.
5. Lader, D. Contraception and sexual health 2008/09. London: Office for National Statistics, 2009.
6. Wellings K. Trends in contraceptive use since 1970. *British Journal of Family Planning.* 1986;12:15–22.
7. Department of Health and Social Security. *Contraceptive Advice and Treatment of Young People Under 16.* Health Circular HC 86; 1986.

8. Population Information Program. IUDs: An update. *Population Reports.* 1995;6:9.
9. Pappenheim K. Emergency contraception provision in the UK. *Planned Parenthood in Europe.* 1995;24:20–22.
10. UNICEF, *A League Table of Teenage Births in Rich Countries.* Florence, Italy: UNICEF Innocenti Centre; July 2002.
11. UK abortion Law, Marie Stopes Clinics International, *http://www.mariestopes.org.uk/Womens_services/Abortion/UK_abortion_law.aspx*
12. Abortion statistics: England and Wales, 2011. (May 2012). *https://www.gov.uk/government/uploads/system/uploads/attachment_data/file/213386/Commentary1.pdf*
13. FDA approves RU 486. *Choices.* 2000;28:32.
14. Sex education in Europe: United Kingdom. *http://www.sexarchive.info/BIB/SexEd/SexEd.html#3.26*
15. UNAIDS Epidemiological Fact Sheets by Country. *http://www.unaids.org/en/regionscountries/countries/unitedkingdomofgreatbritainandnorthernireland/*
16. Latest UK statistics. National AIDS Trust. *http://www.nat.org.uk/HIV-Facts/Statistics/Latest-UK-Statistics.aspx*
17. Terence Higgins Trust: How it all began. *http://www.tht.org.uk/our-charity/About-us/Our-history/How-it-all-began*
18. International Lesbian, Gay, Bisexual, Trans and Intersex Association: United Kingdom. *http://ilga.org/ilga/en/countries/UNITED%20KINGDOM/Articles.*
19. 100 countries and their prostitution policies. *http://prostitution.procon.org/view.resource.php?resourceID=000772#UK*
20. Tart card. *http://en.wikipedia.org/wiki/Tart_card*
21. The English Prostitute Collective. *http://prostitutescollective.net/*
22. Pornography laws: UK. *http://en.wikipedia.org/wiki/Pornography_by_region#United_Kingdom*
23. Petiti, J. *Rights of the Child: Child pornography on the Internet.* United Nations Economic and Social Council, December 24, 2004.
24. UK wants to restrict access to online porn. CNN.com, July 22, 2013. *http://www.cnn.com/2013/07/22/tech/web/uk-porn-ban-cameron/index.html*

UNITED STATES

1. Worldwide Ages of Consent. *http://www.avert.org/age-of-consent.htm.*
2. Facts on American teens' sexual and reproductive health, 2012. Guttmacher Institute. *http://www.guttmacher.org/pubs/FB-ATSRH.html.*
3. Singh S, Darroch J. Adolescent pregnancy and childrearing: Levels and trends in developed countries. *Family Planning Perspectives.* 2000;32:14–23.
4. Darroch J, Singh S, Frost J, Study Team. Differences in teenage pregnancy rates among five developed countries: The roles of sexual activity and contraceptive use. *Family Planning Perspectives.* 2001;33:244–250 & 281.
5. Martinez G et al., Teenagers in the United States: sexual activity, contraceptive use, and childbearing, 2006–2010 *National Survey of Family Growth, Vital and Health Statistics,* 2011, Series 23, No. 31.
6. Guttmacher Institute, Minors' access to contraceptive services, *State Policies in Brief* (as of May 2013), 2013, *http://www.guttmacher.org/statecenter/spibs/spib_MACS.pdf*
7. Santelli J et al., Transnational comparisons of adolescent contraceptive use: What can we learn from these comparisons? *Archives of Pediatrics & Adolescent Medicine,* 2008, 162(1):92–94.

8. McKay A et al., Trends in teen pregnancy rates from 1996–2006: a comparison of Canada, Sweden, USA and England/Wales, *Canadian Journal of Human Sexuality*, 19(1–2):43–52.

9. Torres A, Forrest J. Family planning clinic services in the United States. *Family Planning Perspectives*. 1985;17:30.

10. The Emergency Contraception Website. *http://ec.princeton.edu/*.

11. Petchesky RP. *Abortion and Women's Choice*. Boston: Northeastern University Press; 1985.

12. Center for Reproductive Rights. 2011 *Midyear legislative wrap up. http://reproductiverights.org/wn_abortion.html.*

13. Guttmacher Institute, Parental involvement in minors' abortions, *State Policies in Brief* (as of May 2013), 2013 *http://www.guttmacher.org/statecenter/spibs/spib_PIMA.pdf*

14. Guttmacher Institute, Facts on induced abortion in the United States, July 2013. *http://www.guttmacher.org/pubs/fb_induced_abortion.html*

15. FDA approves RU 486. Choices. 2000;28:32.

16. The Future of Sex Education. History of sex education. *http://www.futureofsexed.org/background.html*

17. Sexuality Information and Education Council of the United States (SIECUS). Public support for comprehensive sexuality education. *http://www.siecus.org/index.cfm?fuseaction = Page.ViewPage&PageID = 1197*

18. Advocates for Youth. Comprehensive sex education: Research and results. *http://www.advocatesforyouth.org/publications/1487?task = view*

19. Advocates for Youth. Effective sex education. *http://www.advocatesforyouth.org/publications/450?task = view*

20. The National Coalition for the Support of Sexuality Education. *http://www.ncsse.com/*

21. The Future of Sex Education. National sexuality education standards: Core content and skills, K-12. http://www.futureofsexed.org/index.html

22. UNAIDS Epidemiological Fact Sheets by Country. *http://www.unaids.org/en/regionscountries/countries/unitedstatesofamerica/*

23. Office of the Surgeon General. The Surgeon General's Call to Action to Promote Sexual Health and Responsible Sexual Behavior 2001. *http://www.surgeongeneral.gov/library.*

24. Advocates for Youth. Adolescent sexual health in Europe and the US. *http://www.advocatesforyouth.org/component/content/article/419-adolescent-sexual-health-in-europe-and-the-us*

25. Herrell R. The symbolic strategies of the Chicago's Gay and Lesbian Pride Day Parade. In Herdt G, ed. *Gay Culture in America*. Boston: Beacon Press; 1992.

26. Freedom to Marry. The States. *http://www.freedomtomarry.org/states/*

27. Reilly, R. Supreme Court DOMA decision rules federal same-sex marriage ban unconstitutional. Huffington Post. June 26, 2013. *http://www.huffingtonpost.com/2013/06/26/supreme-court-doma-decision_n_3454811.html*

28. Lambda Legal. Lawrence v. Texas. *http://www.lambdalegal.org/in-court/cases/lawrence-v-texas*

29. Banes, J.E. Military gay ban to end in 60 days. Wall Street Journal. July 22, 2011. *http://online.wsj.com/article/SB10001424053111903554904576460463874043414.html*

30. Prostitutes' Education Network. *http://www.bayswan.org/penet.html.*

31. Kelly G. *Sexuality Today: A Human Perspective 8th edition*. New York: McGraw-Hill; 2006: 464.

32. Feminists for free Expression. Feminism and Free Speech: Pornography. *http://www.ffeusa.org/html/statements/statements_pornography.html.*

33. Strong B, DeVault C, Sayad BW., Yarber, W. *Human Sexuality, 5th edition*. New York: McGraw-Hill; 2006: 660–661.

VIETNAM

1. Worldwide Ages of Consent. *http://www .avert.org/age-of-consent.htm.*
2. Parent-child discussions about sexuality are uncommon in Vietnam. June 2011, International perspectives on sexual and reproductive health. *http://www.guttmacher .org/pubs/journals/3710311.html*
3. Vietnam's Two-Child Policy. *http://news.bbc .co.uk/2/hi/asia-pacific/1011799.stm*
4. Thang, N.M. & Anh, D.N. (2002). Accessibility and use of contraceptives in Vietnam. International Family Planning Perspectives, 28. *http://www.guttmacher .org/pubs/journals/2821402.html.*
5. Vietnam's high abortion rate, lack of sex education among young people. *http://www.medicalnewstoday.com/articles/ 27187.php.*
6. Vietnam's abortion rate very high. *http://english.vietnamnet.vn/social/2009/04/ 843066/*
7. Sex education café opens in Hanoi. UN Wire. *http://www.unwire.org/unwire/ 19991222/6460_story.asp.*
8. UNAIDS Epidemiological Fact Sheets by Country. *http://www.unaids.org/en/ regionscountries/countries/vietnam/*
9. Vietnamese LGBT advocates to celebrate benchmark year. Voice of America. August 2, 2013. *http://www.voanews.com/content/ vietnam-gay-rights-community-to-celebrate -benchmark-year/1722596.html*
10. Vietnam: A leader on LGBT Rights in Asia. International Herald tribune. March 13, 2013. *http://latitude.blogs.nytimes.com/2013/03/ 12/vietnam-a-leader-on-l-g-b-t-rights-in-asia/*
11. UNIAP—Who is being trafficked in Vietnam? No-Trafficking.org *http://www .no-trafficking.org/vietnam_who.html*
12. Pornography laws in Vietnam. *http://en.wikipedia.org/wiki/Pornography _by_region*

12. Pornography laws in Vietnam. *http://en.wikipedia.org/wiki/Pornography _by_region*

ZIMBABWE

1. Worldwide Ages of Consent. *http://www .avert.org/age-of-consent.htm.*
2. Kim YM. Promoting sexual responsibility among young people in Zimbabwe. International Family Planning Perspectives. 2001;27:11–18.
3. Basset M. Zimbabwe: The social roots of AIDS. *UNESCO Courier,* June 1995.
4. Henderson C. Condom vending machine joins fight against AIDS. *AIDS Weekly.* September 1992.
5. Center for Reproductive Laws and Policy. Reproductive Rights 2000: Moving Forward. *http://reproductiverights.org.*
6. UNFPA—Zibabwe: A success story. March 16, 2011. *http://www.unfpa.org/public/home/ news/pid/7382*
7. UNAIDS Epidemiological Fact Sheets by Country. *http://www.who.int/hiv/pub/ epidemiology/pubfacts/en/.*
8. Robert Mugabe, Zimbabwe President, threatens to behead gay citizens. The Huffington Post, July 26. 2013. *http://www.huffingtonpost.com/2013/07/ 26/mugabe-zimbabwe-behead-gays_n _3659454.html*
9. International Lesbian, Gay, Bisexual, Trans and Intersex Association: Zimbabwe. *http://ilga.org/ilga/en/countries/ZIMBABWE/ Articles.*
10. MDC pushing to legalize prostitution. Zimbabwe Community Network. December 16, 2011. *http://nzcn.wordpress.com/2011/ 12/16/mdc-pushing-to-legalize-prostitution/*

INTERNATIONAL RESOURCES RELATED TO SEXUALITY

Guttmacher Institute
Publishes *International Family Planning Perspectives*
120 Wall Street, 21st floor
New York, NY 10005
USA
Tel: 212/248-1111
Website: *http://www.guttmacher.org*

International Gay and Lesbian Human Rights Commission
80 Maiden Lane, Suite 1505
New York, NY 10038
USA
Tel: 212/268-8040
Website: *http://www.iglhrc.org*

International Planned Parenthood Federation (IPPF)
4 Newhams Row
London SE1 3UZ
ENGLAND
Tel: 44-(0)20-7939-8200
Website: *http://www.ippf.org*

United Nations Joint Programme on AIDS (UNAIDS)
20 Avenue Appia 1211
Geneva 27
SWITZERLAND
Tel: 41-22-791-3666
Website: *http://www.unaids.org*

United Nations Population Fund (UNFPA)
220 East 42nd Street
New York, NY 10017
USA
Tel: 212/297-5000
Website: *http://www.unfpa.org*

World Association of Sexual Health
Tezoquipa 26
Colonia La Joya
Delegacion Tlalapan
Mexico D.F. 14000
Mexico
Website: *http://www.worldsexology.org*

World Health Organization (WHO)
20 Avenue Appia 1211
Geneva 27
SWITZERLAND
Tel: 41-22-791-2111
Website: *http://www.who.int/en*